The Musée des Arts et Métiers

Musée des Arts et Métiers
60 rue Réaumur, 75003 Paris
Open every day, except Mondays
and holidays, from 10 a.m. to 6 p.m.
Thursdays open till 9 p.m.
Tel: 01 40 27 22 20
Fax: 01 40 27 26 62

MUSÉES ET MONUMENTS DE FRANCE

COLLECTION DIRECTED BY PIERRE LEMOINE

# The Musée des Arts et Métiers

Dominique Ferriot
Director

Bruno Jacomy
Deputy Director

Louis André
Curator

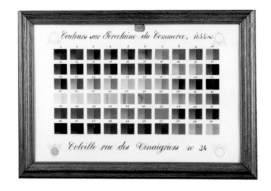

Fondation BNP PARIBAS

Musée des Arts et Métiers

Réunion des Musées nationaux

*Cover:*
*The Dulcimer Player,* a musical automaton made
in 1784. See fig. 104, p. 101.

*Frontispiece:*
Model of a locomobile which can travel by road
(detail), 19th century. Inv. 16694

*Page 3:*
Porcelain plate showing colour samples
by Colville, Paris, 1855. Inv. 6617

*Acknowledgements*

The authors wish to thank the museum staff and more especially:

Hamidul Alam, Anne-Laure Carré, Jean-Luc Chazoule, Marie-Sophie Corcy, Stéphanie
Courtois, Frédérique Desvergnes, Elisabeth Drye, Michèle Henri Pasquet, Alain Mercier,
Nathalie Naudi, Nicolas Neiertz, Denis Pruvrel, Natalie Schindler, Isabelle Taillebourg.

# Foreword

Founded in 1794 by Henri Grégoire, a constitutional priest and deputy at the Convention, the Conservatoire des arts et métiers was intended as a 'repository for new and useful machines' which were to be displayed to artisans and curious members of the public. The very first technical and industrial museum, in the nineteenth century it developed into a Pantheon of technical inventions. The collection, which was regularly added to, especially for teaching purposes, was unique. Calculating machines by Pascal, marine chronometers by Berthoud, pendulums by Foucault, planes by Ader, Breguet and Blériot, cameras, early film cameras, engines, tools, models and drawings…, the collection gradually became so rich that it was a burden for the Conservatoire. During the twentieth century the Museum was forgotten and became a refuge for enraptured wanderers such as Julien Green, Hector Bianciotti and Umberto Eco.

Now, after ten years of patient work led by a team of engineers, historians, architects and draughtsmen, the Musée des arts et métiers has been reborn and a brand new display will take the visitor on a journey through technical history and the Museum's collections. This book takes the reader on that same journey through time, rediscovering the talents of mankind and the ingenuity of his achievements. The renovated Musée des arts et métiers remains faithful to the spirit of those who founded it, transforming a remarkable historical site, the old abbey of Saint-Martin-des-Champs, into a temple to invention and a school for the imagination. Progress is no longer a religion, however, and we retrace a more complex route, one marked by trial and error, yet which clearly illustrates the spirit of adventure that is still the keystone of the Museum today.

I would like to thank Fondation BNP Paribas which, as an active member of the Association des Amis du Musée, made possible this publication, and in so doing greatly contributed to making known this unique collection.

Dominique Ferriot
Director of the Musée des arts et métiers

# History of the Museum

## A Conservatory for the Arts and Crafts

'I have come to show you how to improve national industry.' With these words, on 29 September 1794, Henri Grégoire, deputy at the Convention, proposed 'the creation of a Conservatory for the arts and crafts in which all newly invented or improved tools and machines will be gathered'. 'There will be no dogma: experience and observation alone will be our guide. We must enlighten ignorance that knows not and poverty that has no means of acquiring knowledge. The craftsman, who has seen only his workshop, cannot dream of anything better. The project we are presenting to you will offer him the means to compete and to realise his talents. He who can only be an imitator will be able to correct his technique through the knowledge of good examples. He who can see further will make new connections, for all the arts have points of contact. Thus you will increase both the sum of knowledge and the number of those who know.' In this speech, Grégoire made clear the aim and the structure of the new Conservatory: 'We will choose a spacious building, part of which can be used as a lecture hall. Instruments and models from all the arts whose purpose is to feed, clothe and house will be gathered there. The accumulation of useless machines will be avoided. Only the best example of each kind will be allowed to feature in this repository.' Thus, since its inception, the Conservatoire des arts et métiers has had a twofold purpose: conservation and education. 'Teaching, which will take place alongside the models, requires demonstrators. In fact, all the departments must contribute to the good of this establishment, because the National Convention has no favourites: everyone has the same rights … The Conservatory will be a reservoir whose canals will fertilise the whole of France. Drawings, descriptions, even models of whatever may have the hallmark of usefulness will be distributed throughout every region.'

## A Non-Conformist Priest

Born in Vého in 1750, Henri Grégoire became the parish priest of Ember-ménil, and attracted attention as early as 1788 with his *Essai sur la régénération physique, morale et politique des Juifs* ('Essay on the physical, moral and political regeneration of the Jews'). A deputy of the clergy at the Estates-General, he contributed towards the union of the lower clergy and the Third Estate. The first priest to take the oath of loyalty demanded by the civil constitution, he also became the first constitutional bishop of Blois. He fought to defend the rights of 'coloured people', to use his own expression: 'At the moment when the French have revived

2. Abbé Henri Grégoire (1750–1831), founder of the Conservatoire des arts et métiers

1. The 'Museum of machines in action' in the chapel, from the journal *La Nature*, 1880

liberty, do they dare to sanction the slavery of their brothers?' A member of the Committee of Public Instruction, Grégoire protected the national heritage against what he described as 'vandalism', and called for the creation of public libraries and the preservation of botanical gardens. 'Libraries and museums established with care are, so to speak, the workshops of the human mind. We must now revolutionise the arts, collect all the materials and their means of production, and hand down this heritage to future generations.' To complete his educational work, Grégoire applied himself to bringing the French language into widespread use. 'The ability to read, write and speak in the national language is indispensable knowledge for all French citizens.' In the scientific sphere, he was involved in the creation of the Board of Longitude, which was founded in 1795 to improve navigation and advance astronomy. With the creation of the Conservatoire des arts et métiers, he laid the foundations for the technical teaching which was the original feature of an institution in which he, together with Molard and Conté, was one of the first demonstrators. Passionately devoted to ideas of justice and equality, Henri Grégoire remained faithful to Revolutionary ideals until his death in 1831. 'My voice and my pen have never ceased to claim the imprescriptible rights of suffering humanity without making any distinction on grounds of climate, colour or race.' His ashes were moved to the Pantheon during the celebrations of the bicentenary of the French Revolution.

### Saint-Martin-des-Champs

In 1798, this constitutional priest proposed that a church should be made available to the Conservatoire des arts et métiers, which had been lodged in makeshift premises since its creation in 1794. The abbey of Saint-Martin-des-Champs was chosen 'as a matter of urgency' by the Council of the Five Hundred. Numerous artisans lived in the area, the buildings were vast and would at last enable the models – which had been piling up in three different repositories – to be studied. Thus, saved from certain destruction, the buildings of Saint-Martin-des-Champs were about to experience a new future.

A place of worship steeped in history, the abbey is more than a thousand years old. In his *Histoire des Francs* Grégoire de Tours mentions the existence of an oratory dedicated to Saint Martin which was miraculously spared when a fire ravaged the city in 585. The abbey of Saint-Martin, which existed at the beginning of the eighth century, was destroyed by Norman invaders in the ninth century and rebuilt in 1060 by Henry I. A dependency of the abbey of Cluny, the priory of Saint-Martin-des-Champs became a renowned and prosperous monastery. The church was gradually embellished as the years went by and, in the 17th century, François Mansart furnished it with a high altar, the foundations of which were rediscovered during excavation work in 1993. The dig brought to *3* light remains from different eras, notably traces of the Merovingian basilica whose basement contained a wealth of ornamented stone and plaster sarcophagi. Thus, the Revolutionary authorities chose a site steeped in religious history to set up a new kind of institution, one dedicated to technical progress and industrial innovation.

*3.* Archaeological excavations in the chapel of the former abbey of Saint-Martin-des-Champs: Merovingian sarcophagi found under 19th-century water pipes

## The Birth of a Collection

'We will establish in Paris, under the name Conservatoire des arts et métiers, a repository for machines, models, tools, drawings, descriptions and books belonging to every category of art and craft. The original versions of invented or improved instruments and machines will be deposited in the Conservatoire' (decree of 10 October 1794). The collection included machines bequeathed to Louis XVI in 1782 by the mechanist Jacques Vaucanson. These machines were already on display to a curious public at the Hôtel de Mortagne in the rue de Charonne, a building assigned to the purpose of demonstrating new and useful machines, the need for which was clear to the 'enlightened'.

Vaucanson (1709–1782) was known for his celebrated automata *(The Flute*

*Player, The Tambourine and Flageolet Player, The Digesting Duck)* which disappeared in the nineteenth century. Most of all, however, he revolutionised the silk industry in France by inventing new machines and the machine-tools needed to build them. These machines were of course acquired by the Conservatoire des arts et métiers: a loom, a machine for making chains, a mill for processing organzine, an iron slide lathe, the first large machine built with an iron frame.

The Conservatoire also inherited earlier physics collections. In 1792, the physicist Jacques-Cesar-Alexandre Charles (1746–1823) bequeathed to the nation more than 330 items, including the instruments he had bought from Abbé Nollet. We will come across these instruments again later in the exhibition galleries, along with the models of machines and parts used in clockmaking, which were bequeathed by Pajot d'Ons-en-Bray in 1753 and include instruments from the Académie des sciences and assets confiscated during the turbulent days of the French Revolution.

The establishment of the Conservatoire des arts et métiers at Saint-Martin-des-Champs, where it opened in 1800, at last gave a permanent home to pieces which had until then been scattered and ill-organised. And so it was that Cugnot's steam-driven dray, the *fardier* (1771), left the Arsenal for the Conservatoire.

This great initiative was also an opportunity to have the insides of machines drawn along with details of their mechanisms. A unique collection of technical drawings was gradually established; draughtsmen ap-

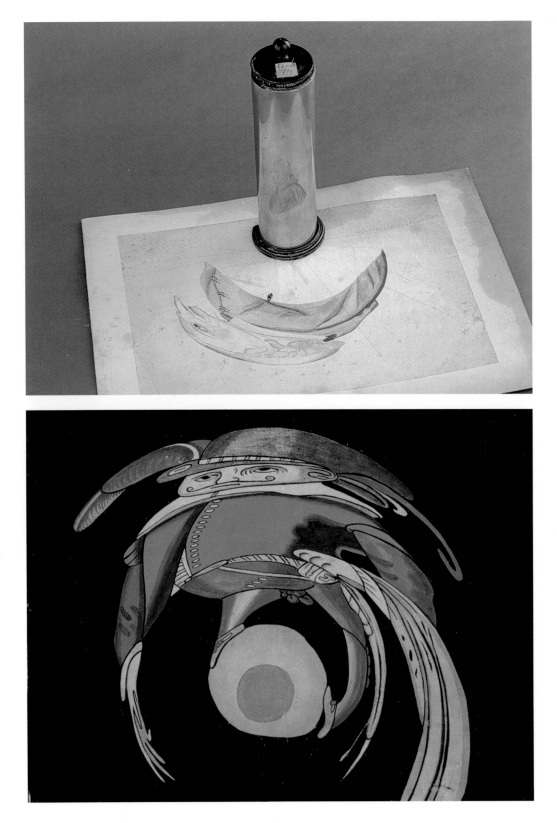

5. Cylindrical mirror and
drawing for an anamorphosis
from the collection of the
physicist Jacques-César-
Alexandre Charles, 18th
century. Inv. 794 and 1747

6. An anamorphosis from
the collection of the physicist
Jacques-César-Alexandre
Charles, 18th century.
Inv. 1745

pointed by the institution – Dromard, Beuvelot and Goussier – created masterpieces of aesthetics and precision that have fortunately come down to us in a very good state of preservation. The portfolio of industrial drawings, the oldest part of which is known as 'Vaucanson's portfolio' in homage to the illustrious mechanist, is one of the highlights of the Museum's collection. Numerous plates illustrate the objects in the collection and represent an irreplaceable source of information about technical history and instruments.

7. A rail is installed in the exhibition galleries in the 19th century. Display case of Emile Gallé's work

### The Museum and Education

Once the Conservatoire was finally established, the collection kept on growing. The general catalogue drawn up in 1818 by its director, Gérard-Joseph Christian, gives a precise account of the wealth of the institution. Open to the public on Thursdays and Sundays, and to scholars, artists and foreigners every other day, the exhibition galleries already displayed a number of the highlights of the modern Museum. Agriculture and industry constituted the main parts of the display, and there was a clearly identified set of scientific instruments, including the pieces bequeathed in 1807 by the clockmaker Ferdinand Berthoud (1727–1807).

In 1819 a new era began for the Conservatoire with the establishment of the first teaching posts. Demonstrating how machines worked and drawing basic mechanisms no longer seemed to be enough as a strategy to improve French industry. A proper system of technical education was required. The first three chairs were awarded to Charles Dupin for 'mechanics applied to the arts', Nicolas Clément-Desormes for chemistry, and Jean-Baptiste Say for industrial economy, and these men were to have a lasting influence on the future direction of the institution. The

26

links between the collections and the holders of these academic posts were very close throughout the nineteenth century. A rail-track was set up in the exhibition galleries to make it easier to move objects to the lecture halls and classrooms. The professors were also demonstrators and initiated the acquisition of numerous items intended specifically for teaching purposes. In this way an important series of wire models used as an aid in teaching mathematics was devised at the request of Théodore Olivier (1793–1853), professor of descriptive geometry. Some display cases were even bought to house models made during lessons.

8. 'The storehouse of discovery'.
The Musée des arts et métiers before the renovation

One example of this is a piece of furniture, designed by Guérin and featuring splendid inlaid work, which was put together thanks to Professor Lucien Magne, who held the chair of applied arts, founded in 1898.
As well as being a teaching tool the Museum – this term is now appropriate – was also a place of research and experimentation. Through the impetus given by General Morin, director of the Conservatoire from 1852 to 1880, the chapel became a veritable laboratory. Thanks to a water-tank installed in the bell-tower, hydraulic machines could be set in motion. Two steam engines in the church drove the rest of the machinery in a miniature factory. People at the time marvelled – a 'museum of machines in action' wrote Gaston Tissandier in *La Nature* – or professed horror: a 'church turned into a warehouse' claimed Strindberg on discovering to his alarm the statue of Papin located in the choir in the place of the altar (*Nuits de somnambule par jours éveillés,* 1883). On 29 October 1864, the director organised a special performance, setting in motion Caselli's pantelegraph, Froment's electric sorter and De La Rive's device which reproduced the northern lights. With the spectacle of the machines in the chapel, the collection as a whole testified to the greatness and originality of the institution.

LE " BLÉRIOT " AUX ARTS ET MÉTIERS
Arrivée de Monsieur BLÉRIOT aux Arts et Métiers

## The Pantheon of Technical Inventions

On 13 October 1909, the *Blériot XI* made its ceremonial entrance into the Museum. A few months after Louis Blériot's heroic crossing of the Channel, his plane had earned its place of honour among the inventions preserved at the Conservatoire des arts et métiers, now a true Pantheon of technical inventions. Close by were other exceptional pieces: the first aeroplane, designed by Clément Ader (1897); pendulums made by Léon Foucault in 1851 and 1855; looms by Bouchon, Falcon and Jacquard, acquired after the Universal Exhibition of 1855; the magnificent series of models made by the Deering Harvester Company to demonstrate the improvements made to harvesting machines throughout the 19th century, and which were also acquired after a Universal Exhibition, this time the one held in 1900. These were only a few of the tens of thousands of objects in this repository of 'new and useful inventions', to use the Revolutionary description.

The architecture of the building was adapted to suit the needs of the institution. Léon Vaudoyer, the Conservatoire's architect from 1838 to 1872, created a new monumental entrance in the rue Saint-Martin, and erected a building for the industrial collection to match the monks' former refectory, which was now a library. Vaudoyer also commissioned allegorical figures representing art, science and industry and placed statues of Vaucanson and Olivier de Serres on either side of the grand staircase leading to the first-floor galleries. Soon imitated by the Science Museum in London and later by the Deutsches Museum in Munich, founded in 1903, the Musée du Conservatoire des arts et métiers was the first of a series of industrial museums designed to preserve the technical heritage and encourage innovation.

## Chronicle of a Renovation

How then can we explain the subsequent decline of the Museum in the mid-twentieth century and the state of neglect it was in only ten years ago? As science teaching became more abstract, the goals of conservation and demonstration had progressively moved apart. The collection, a source of enrichment and influence for the Conservatoire, had become a heavy burden and the 'museum of working machines' an unchanging universe with a strange and sometimes disturbing charm. 'You enter and are stunned by a conspiracy in which the sublime universe of heavenly ogives and the chtonian world of gas guzzlers are juxtaposed.' This is how Umberto Eco describes the chapel of the Museum in *Foucault's Pendulum* (1988). Like Julien Green and Hector Bianciotti before him, Eco defends and glorifies a Museum without equal, one in which the very dust should be preserved. But, in spite of its reputation and the wealth of its unique collection (80,000 objects, 15,000 drawings demonstrating technical creativity from the 16th to the present century), the Museum had lost its public, it was no longer maintained by the Conservatoire, and the 'Louvre des techniques' was slowly dying. Faced with a crisis situation, and as had been the case two hundred years before, a programme of major works was decided on and a team of historians and engineers specified the path the renovated Museum should follow.

In 1989 Pierre Piganiol's report recommended that a repository be created in a nearby suburb and that it should be open to the public, in other words accessible to researchers and more generally to those involved in study projects or conservation. The store, built on the Plaine-Saint-Denis by the architect François Deslaugiers, is now open to 'enlightened'

9. Blériot's plane makes its formal entrance into the Conservatoire des arts et métiers, 13 October 1909

*10–11.* The collections arranged in the new
repository built in La Plaine-Saint-Denis, 1997

visitors who, on entering the site, encounter a fabulous collection, much of it still unknown. It includes gears, machine-tools, scientific instruments, models, glassware, ceramics, typewriters, printing machines, sewing machines and calculating machines. The repository is both a storehouse and a space where objects, carefully arranged and labelled with barcodes for easy identification and location, have found their place after too many years of being overcrowded and, in some cases, forgotten. Close by, restoration workshops and a photographic studio complete the store's range of attractive and functional facilities.

*12.* A copper 'Nautilus', drawing by François Schuiten for the refurbishment of the 'Arts et Métiers' métro station, 1994

Since 1994 the Museum has also been present on the Internet. Its web-site covers the whole collection and features animated sequences and virtual visits. To complement or prepare for a visit to the Museum, written and electronic sources are available (quarterly reviews, educational pamphlets, CD-ROM). Thus informed, we can begin our visit to the new Musée des arts et métiers.

## A Museum of Technical Innovation

Before going into the Museum, get off at the Arts et Métiers métro station. In this subterranean world you will discover illustrations of the seven technical domains that structure the permanent exhibition: an armillary sphere representing the scientific instrument, a converter by Thomas for the section on materials, the model of the Antoinette bridge for construction, the *Telstar* satellite for communications, a hydraulic wheel for energy, a system of gears for mechanical engineering and a strange flying machine, the *Avisol*, for transport. Commissioned by the RATP (Parisian transport authority), the stage designer François Schuiten conceived a métro station with walls completely covered in a copper lin-  *12* ing. Its rounded forms and metallic colours vividly evoke the world and symbols of the Museum, located just above your head.

*13.* Model of the chemistry laboratory (detail) made in 1783 by François-Etienne Calla at the request of Madame de Genlis. Inv. 131

At the entrance, Gramme will catch your eye. Leaning on his dynamo,  *91* he is a sign to visitors that they are entering a world of invention and ingenuity.

The new exhibition design suggested by the staff at the Museum and by Andrea Bruno, the architect behind the renovation work, aims to make visitors aware of the spirit of those who made or improved the 'flagship objects' in the collection, as well as the series of objects marking out the proposed visiting trail. Among these inventors are women such as Madame Lavoisier, the faithful helper in the work of the man who founded modern chemistry, and Madame de Genlis, governess of the future Louis-Philippe and his sister Adélaide. It was she who had the Périer brothers create extraordinary models representing the arts and crafts at  *13* the time of Diderot's *Encyclopédie*. There are also instrument-makers such as Papin, Fortin and Froment without whom the works of scientists such as Huygens, Lavoisier and Foucault might not have been possible. Finally, there are the demonstrators whose past experience guides us through the new displays.

# The Scientific Instrument

Advances in scientific knowledge owe much to the great men who, at key points in history, formulated hypotheses which were sometimes difficult to accept, then demonstrated the validity of their theories by means of striking experiments. To carry out this essential experimentation, they used, as they still do, instruments made with an ingenuity, precision and innovation that compels admiration. The Musée des arts et métiers can be proud of housing one of the most remarkable collections of these tools. In the galleries dedicated to the scientific instrument, the Museum pays homage not only to the great scholars who changed our vision of the world, but also to these 'invisible technicians' who, alongside the scientists, and too often in their shadow, designed and constructed astrolabes, scales, microscopes and telescopes, without which the dimensions of the world would still seem very limited.

## Man Measures the Dimensions of the World

Scientific instruments have existed since Antiquity, since man first tried to find the answers to such everyday matters as how to measure a field, observe the movements of the stars or the passing of time in clepsydrae. But a great step forward was made at the end of the Renaissance, in a Europe eager to acquire knowledge of the world, of natural phenomena and of the human body. The seventeenth century, an age of science in which observation was limited to the dimensions of the eye-piece of a telescope, was followed by the age of the spectacle, with the Enlightenment and the industrial revolution. The cabinet gave way to the laboratory, instruments became everyday objects, and today we use sensors, watches and speedometers often without even knowing it.

The collections displayed in the Musée des arts et métiers encourage the visitor to become more familiar with the history of science, to understand and assimilate it. The journey that began with the astrolabe, the forerunner of scientific instruments, is far from over. The adventure continues. Towards the end of the sixteenth century Gualterus Arsenius (*c.* 1530–1580), the Flemish astrolabe maker, was adding the finishing touches to his instruments, which were known and valued for their precision by astronomers all over Europe. The Museum has two astrolabes from his workshop.

Originally invented by Arab instrument-makers and astronomers in the first centuries after Christ, astrolabes became ever more precise – they also became increasingly complex. The astrolabe, an instrument for observing and for calculating, made it possible to measure the height of the sun on the horizon, and to calculate the time and the place of the sun in the zodiac. The favoured instrument of astronomers and astrologers, the

*15.* Large astrolabe by Gualterus Arsenius, 1569. Height: 50 cm. Inv. 3902

*14.* Clockwork celestial sphere, made by the Swiss clockmaker Jost Bürgi, *c.* 1580. Height: 56 cm. Inv. 7490

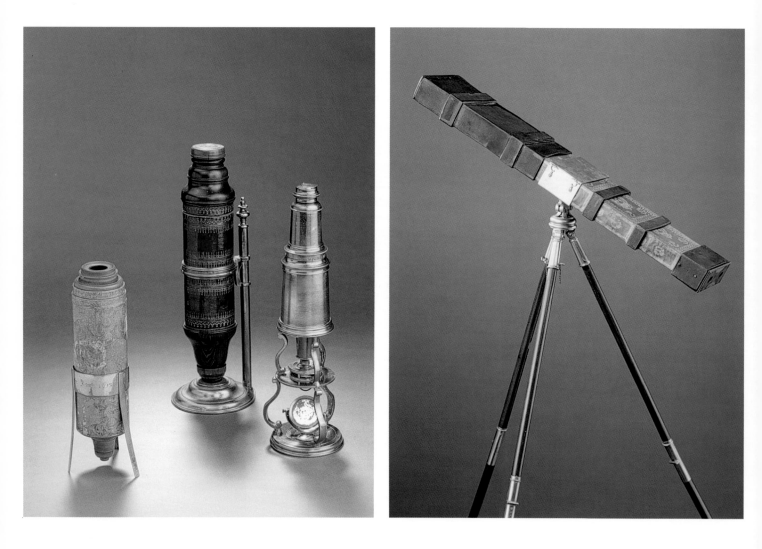

astrolabe was also essential in teaching the movements of the stars. But because of the complexity of the small-scale cosmos represented on its surface, the astrolabe could only be used by experts.

To make the representation clearer to beginners, in the Middle Ages skilful technicians began to work on instruments illustrating the heavens in miniature – armillary spheres, for example. The celestial sphere made *14* around 1580 by the Swiss clockmaker Jost Bürgi (1552–1632) is both a clock and a moving representation of the stars grouped into constellations and finely engraved on the surface of a gilded brass sphere. The globe turns in real time and enables the amateur astronomer to locate himself at any time in relation to the heavens.

## Machines with Memories

The complex mechanism hidden inside the sphere itself bears witness to the skill of Renaissance clockmakers. It contrasts strongly with the rather rudimentary mechanisms that can be seen when the cover of another astonishing mechanism, the *Pascaline,* is opened. Blaise Pascal, its creator, *18, 19* was only 19 when he made the first calculating machine in 1642, ten years after Bürgi's death. Its major innovation seems very simple to the twentieth-century observer: it adds or subtracts by automatically performing the carry-over operation. The Rouen clockmaker who constructed the first machines according to Pascal's instructions would have used such precise and delicate mechanisms only when he was making clocks. And yet Pascal's machines brought their creator as much posthumous glory as they did trouble when he was alive. How can a man, people asked, incorporate into a machine this small fragment of memory, this particle of intelligence which is proper to the human race?

In the middle of the great century of scientific discovery, the young Pascal took a great leap forward, and after him many others continued to break down taboos and disobey the established order so that scientific knowledge or techniques could advance. Nearly a century later, it was the turn of Louis-Léon Pajot, Count of Ons-en-Bray (1678–1754), who gave memory to a meteorological instrument. His anemometer, which *20* displays the speed and direction of the wind, features long paper ribbons on which stylets trace the measurements over a period of thirty hours. After the paper has been 'rubbed with a powder of burnt and well-ground deer antlers', it provides the data which the meteorologist can read and analyse later, in order to establish a record of the weather … and perhaps forecast the weather to come.

Pajot's 'pendulum' anemometer – so called because of its clockwork pendulum movement – is only one of his many inventions, but very few of them have survived. His collection contained more than 1700 instruments, machines and various other objects, and was internationally known at the time. Arab princes, the King of Poland, the Duke of Lorraine and princes from the houses of Saxe-Coburg and Saxe-Gotha flocked to his mansion on the rue de Bercy to admire his collections, attend demonstrations or, like Tsar Peter I on 25 March 1717, operate his lathes and other machine-tools.

Although the Museum inherited only a few pieces from Pajot's collection, through the intermediary of the Académie des Sciences, it did acquire thousands of scientific objects from the physics collections of Abbé Jean-Antoine Nollet (1700–1770) and of Jacques-César-Alexandre *87* Charles (1746–1823) which were incorporated very early on. *5, 6, 22*

*16.* Three compound microscopes, late 17th–early 18th century. Inv. 1838, 22309-1, 18101

*17.* Binoculars by Chérubin d'Orléans, 1681. Height: 2.10 m. Inv. 12811

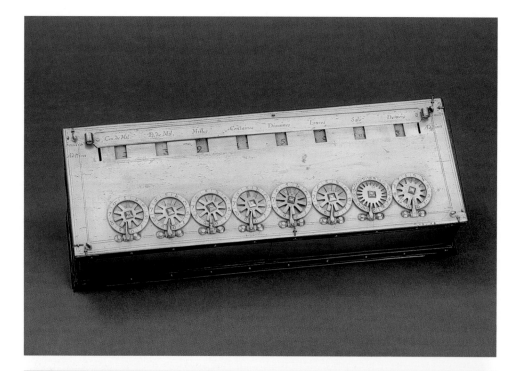

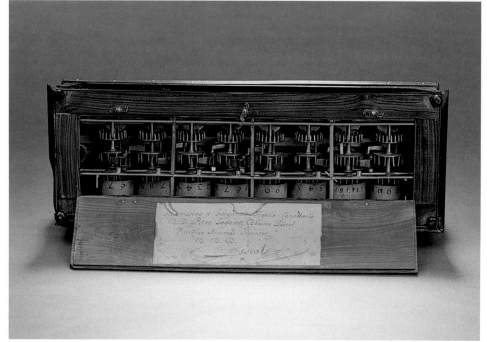

18. Pascal's calculating machine, 1642. Length: 36 cm. Inv. 19600

19. Pascal's calculating machine, detail of the mechanism

20. Recording anemometer invented by Louis-Léon Pajot, Count of Ons-en-Bray, 1734. Height: 2.30 m. Inv. 5608

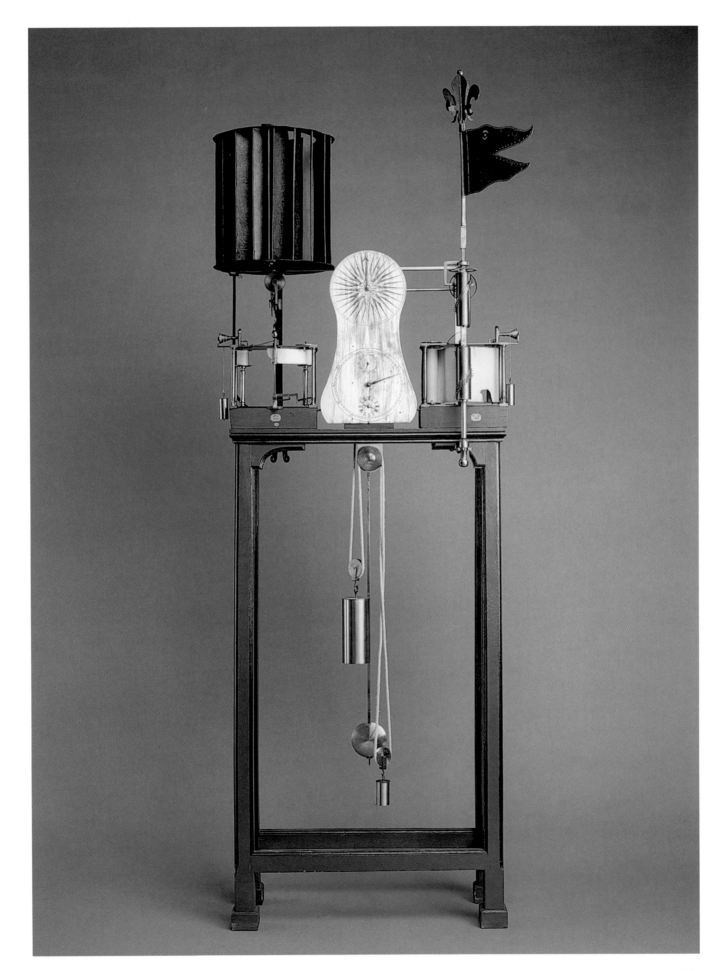

The Musée des arts et métiers not only became the heir to major collections from eighteenth-century cabinets; through the function it fulfills, it is also their descendant. Places where the history of science and machines could be preserved, physics collections were above all intended to ensure that knowledge could be demonstrated and passed on. Many of the machines and instruments in these collections were used in early experiments with electricity – Nairne's machine which demonstrates the kinetic energy of steam, for example, or the *aeolipile,* which was directly inspired by Antique machines devised by the Alexandrian mechanists – or for work on the propagation of light rays or the force of a vacuum. Nollet's air-pump is of particular interest in this context. Because of the vacuum created in the upper bell-jar of the instrument, physicists were

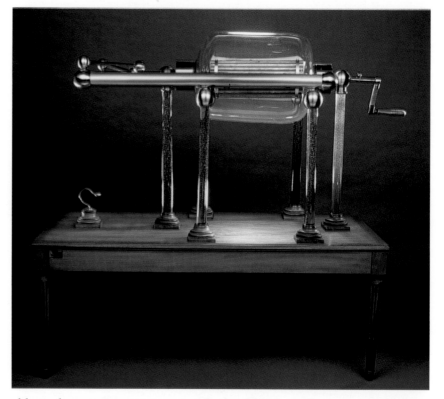

*21.* Electrostatic machine by Nairne, late 18th century. Height: 1.40 m. Inv. 1636

able to demonstrate to an astonished public the still mysterious properties of a vacuum, in which sound could not travel, and whose 'energy of nothingness' could resist enormous forces of traction, as shown by the famous 'Magdeburg hemispheres' experiment, carried out in 1654 by Otto von Guericke (1602–1686) in front of the Diet in Regensburg. All the ingredients – experiments, demonstrations and pleasure, too – which would give birth to the Conservatoire in the unstable climate of the Revolution were already present.

## The Quest for Precision

Methods of measuring time and space have been particularly important in the long history of scientific instruments. Several of the great adventures of the human race owe much to instruments enabling the user to find his bearings in space and time. These include the major discoveries associated with maritime navigation. For many years, mariners' astrolabes, followed by octants and sextants, together with the hourglass and later the marine chronometer, were used to work out one's position at sea, in other words, to determine the latitude and, especially, the longitude.

*22.* Ivory acrobat from Jacques-César-Alexandre Charles' collection. Height: 28 cm. Inv. 1488

26

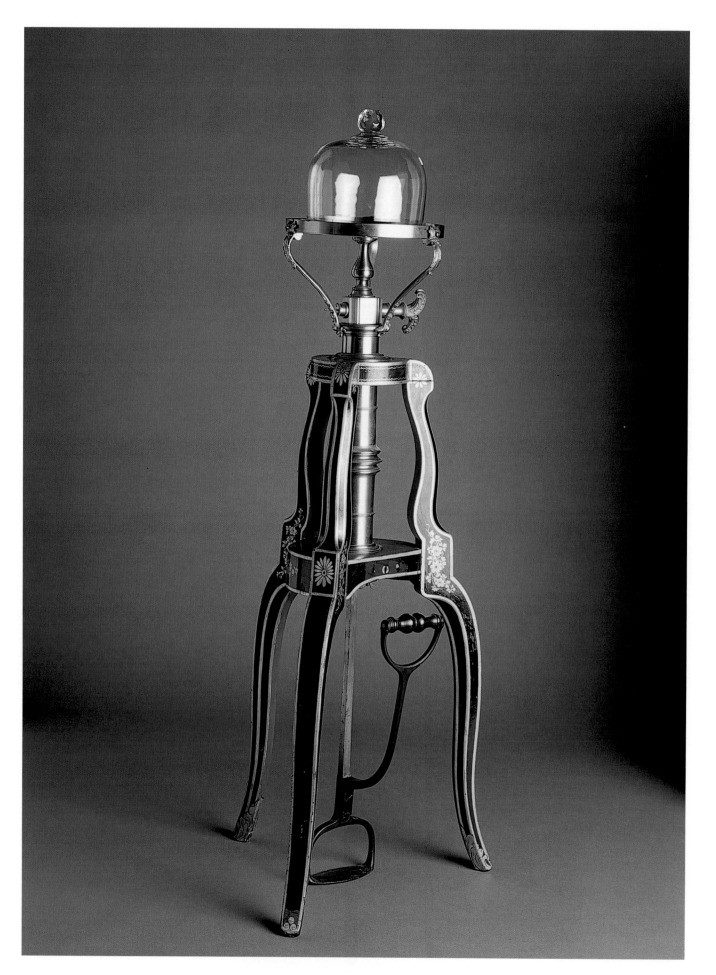

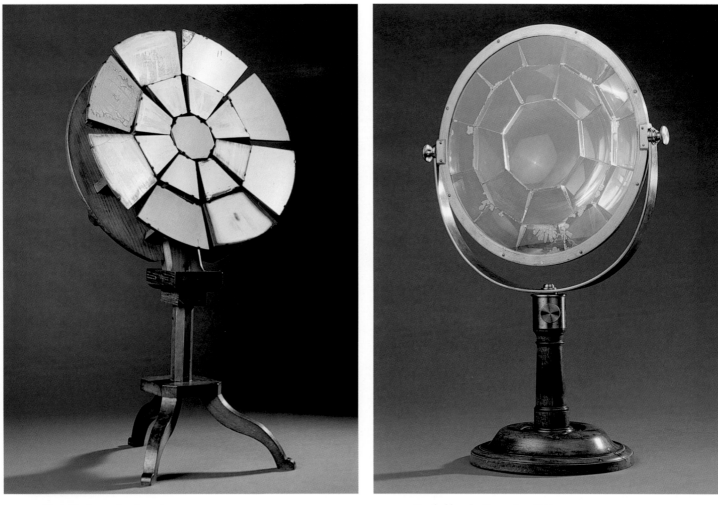

*24.* Variable-focus circular mirror
by Buffon. Height: 1.08 m. Inv. 1741

*25.* Graded lens by Fresnel, *c.* 1866.
Height: 69 cm. Inv. 7525

*23.* Air-pump by Nollet. Height: 1.34 m.
Inv. 6923

Considerable advances were made during the eighteenth century in what we would now call the 'high-tech' field of marine chronometry. The incentive for these developments was the fierce competition between France and Britain, battling, as ever, for supremacy at sea, directly linked to the ability to measure time precisely, an essential factor in calculating longitude. As early as 1745, the English clockmaker John Harrison (1693–1776) was awarded the prestigious Copley medal by the Royal Society for a chronometer with two pendulums which was slightly more accurate in telling the time at sea. This was all that was needed to in-

26. Ferdinand Berthoud's marine chronometer number 8, 1767. Height: 41 cm. Inv. 1389–2

27 *Cadil* from Year II, by Fourché. Standard measure of capacity foreshadowing the litre. Height: 26 cm. Inv. 3248

stigate keen competition in France, backed by the Government and marked by ferocious rivalry between the two best clockmakers of the time, the Frenchman Pierre Le Roy (1717–1785) and the Swiss Ferdinand Berthoud (1727–1807).

What remains of this episode is one of the richest collections of marine chronometers, dominated by Le Roy's outstanding instrument, presented to Louis XV in 1766, and Berthoud's marine chronometer number 8, completed in 1767 and tried out at sea the following year. The decisive test for the two chronometers was an Atlantic crossing: they were tried out together in 1771–2 on the frigate the *Flore,* which was on a

*28.* Charlemagne weights, standard royal
prototype made up of 13 weights, bronze,
late 16th century. Height: 19 cm. Inv. 3261

voyage by way of Madeira, Martinique, Newfoundland and Iceland. It was a competition without a winner, but it did confirm the quality of the two chronometers, which although very different in their construction introduced a number of major innovations (escapement systems, compensation for temperature variation and reduction of friction at the pivots) which were later adopted on most precision clocks.

## The Scientific Revolution

Several achievements that still have a bearing on us today emerged from the ferment of ideas during the Enlightenment. Modern chemistry was born in Lavoisier's laboratory, as was an innovation that took many years

29. Laboratory mask, 18th century. Inv. 20492

30. Device for studying the combustion of oils, built by Fortin in 1788 for Antoine Lavoisier's laboratory. Length: 1.30 m. Inv. 7549

31. Antide Janvier's regulator with a universal face and a decimal face, c. 1800. Height: 52 cm. Inv. 10615

to be recognised: the metric and decimal system. The kilogram, the metre, the *cadil* – the original name for the litre – were the tangible elements in this new notion of measurement, which was intended to facilitate commercial as well as scientific business.

The great scientists who thought up this new challenge took their new ideas to their logical conclusion and, after decimalising distance with the metre and weight with the kilogram, it was decided that time should be decimalised as well. Thus, from 22 October 1792, the day was divided into ten hours, the hour into one hundred minutes and the minute into one hundred seconds. Logic had triumphed but clockmakers had to set to work to make new clocks showing decimal as well as sexagesimal time.

The universal regulator, built around 1800 by Antide Janvier (1751–1835), the greatest of the clockmakers in the Franche-Comté region at the time, not only has two faces, for the two systems in use at the time, but also tells the time anywhere in the world, shows the Egyptian calendar (this was the heyday of expeditions to Egypt) and the movements of the heavens. Was it because of the cost involved in the transfer to decimal time, or even because time was thought to be divine, that no one dared to tamper with it? Whatever, the experiment was discreetly brought to an end on 31 December 1805 and would be completely forgotten today if some museums did not have collections of decimal clocks bearing witness in their own way to the implacable logic of the Revolution.

Clockmakers aside – for a long time they were thought of as artists in their own right – few scientific instrument-makers have gone down in history. Who now is familiar with names such as Fortin, Mégnié or Naudin, men who helped Lavoisier build and often design the instruments that made his experiments famous all over Europe? Or Dumoulin-Froment, 'the skilful maker … whose steady hand and light touch have already created so many wonders' eulogised by Léon Foucault (1819–1868), the inventor of the pendulum and the gyroscope, but who left no deep impression on the collective memory?

The quality of the instruments exhibited in the Musée des arts et métiers, and the feeling of excitement associated with them, owes much

to these exceptional men, among them Rudolph Koenig (1832–1901), the 33 maker of many acoustic instruments. They were highly reputed among the scientific community of their day, but posterity has been particularly ungrateful to them.

Contrary to received opinion, scientists are rarely unwilling to undertake menial tasks. Seventeenth-century scientists such as Galileo or Huygens polished the lenses they used for their observations, and twentieth-century physicists spend the best part of their lives perfecting their experiments, keeping up a tradition which links knowledge and knowhow, fundamental science and technical science. The major difference is undoubtedly in terms of scale rather than principle. Modern scientific instruments often use very delicate and elaborate procedures, and the machines themselves require industrial development. Accordingly, the Museum displays lasers, GPS (satellite navigation systems), electron microscopes and other precision instruments which carry information about measurements or position. Finally, it is not uncommon for recent and major discoveries to make use of earlier instruments, thus combining the prestige of pioneering research with ingenious 'tinkering' to perfect innovative scientific instruments. This is the impression notably left by the cyclotron, which helped Pierre and Marie Curie in their pioneering work on particle physics at the Collège de France.

*33.* Koenig's siren, *c.* 1890. Height: 49 cm. Inv. 12610

*32.* Horizontal and vertical pocket sundial, wood, by Stockert, early 18th century. Width: 8.5 cm. Inv. 19279

# Materials

There is no area so up-to-date and yet so ancient as materials. From Neolithic potters to the steel-workers of today, methods of using fire and working with natural materials such as wood and textile fibres have been a key element in human activity. Starting out with raw materials, then *35* fashioning and shaping them, man has worked the materials that give substance to his intellectual concepts as well as his artistic creations. From using crude materials to the increasingly advanced processing of natural materials, synthetic materials came to be created. By means of research aided by scientific instruments – the microscope in particular – man has consistently improved his knowledge of materials, their structure and their composition. As a result, materials can now be chosen according to their potential applications, and can then be combined or used together, making the most of the characteristics and qualities of each.

By presenting in a single display area industrial sectors that are usually separated, the Museum brings to light the factors that unite different materials, through their structure or their mechanical or chemical properties, it shows what guides the choice and the combination of materials used for construction, transformed to receive and transmit energy, or fashioned by the machine-tools of mechanical engineering. In the interaction of the different areas represented here, we find one of the constants of technical history. The exhibition presents both methods of work and the finished products, linking art and technology.

## Wood and Metal

In many areas, materials came to be mastered as early as the Neolithic period, enabling man to meet his most basic requirements: clothing himself and making cooking utensils and agricultural tools. Metal-workers and potters from Antiquity already knew how to extract metal from ore and work out the correct quantity of metal oxide needed to colour enamel. Pre-industrial techniques were quite advanced in many areas and the medieval and Renaissance periods were important in perfecting the use of fire. Entering the second section of the Museum, visitors discover the techniques used at this time for working with materials in such essential areas as wood, glass, iron and textiles.

The method used for working iron, which had been used since Antiquity, changed fundamentally in early eighteenth-century Europe with the transition from the direct to the indirect process. In the latter method, the pig iron is first obtained by smelting in a blast furnace, and is then transformed into iron or steel through a process of decarbonisation. This material, which may have been found by chance, was now in great demand, produced in great quantity and used in ways that took

*34.* Lion and snake made of spun glass, by Lambour, *c.* 1855. Inv. 7009

The skill of ship's carpenters also flourished in the same period with the building of the great vessels of the Royal Navy.

### Textiles, Smelting and Iron, the Origins of the Industrial Revolution

On entering the section of the Museum dealing with materials, the visitor is attracted by the sheer size of Jacques Vaucanson's silk loom. Vaucanson applied his skills as a mechanist and maker of automata to the mechanisation of weaving. The loom features three major innovations: automation, the capacity to be programmed and the movement of the shuttle. It did not have any immediate descendants, however, and suc-

38. Model of a loom designed by Jacques Vaucanson, 1746. Model by Marin, 1855. Inv. 6236.
*Opposite:* detail of the model of Vaucanson's loom

cess came only fifty years later with Jacquard's loom. Vaucanson followed the tradition established by Bouchon and Falcon (models of their looms, dating from 1725 and 1728 respectively, can be seen in the same gallery), but as a brilliant mechanist and automaton-maker, he managed to automate all the operations of the loom. One of the highlights of the collection, the loom emphasises the importance of prototypes in the Museum and its vocation as a museum of innovation.

Vaucanson's research was one aspect of the development in the use of textiles during the eighteenth century, a period which saw the rapid mechanisation of spinning, and later of weaving, changes which ad-

vanced the advent of the Industrial Revolution. In the same period, stimulated by ever-increasing demand, iron metallurgy also underwent a major change with the use of coke for making cast iron, and then of coal for refining it. In this case, the development was more in terms of quantity than quality. Indeed, this new fuel enabled a huge increase in the production of metal. Available in great quantity and more cheaply, new uses were created for it. The famous bridge in Coalbrookdale (1777) represents the earliest use of metal for a large-scale job, and this trend was again evident a few years later in the dome of the corn exchange and the Pont des Arts in Paris. The blast-furnace increased both in production capacity and in complexity, as can be seen in the 1847 model by Eugène *41* Philippe, one of the main designers of models for the Conservatoire's galleries during the July Monarchy. It shows the recently adopted device for recovering the gases that escape from the throat of the furnace. They were used to heat the air which stoked the blast-furnace, or the furnace

in a forge, thus enabling invaluable savings in fuel and heating the water in the boilers that fed the steam-engines. From then on, these engines powered the bellows, hammers and rolling mills of the great iron and steel factories.

The rolling mill in fact replaced the classic hammer in the refining of iron and also enabled finished products to be put together in the factory; these products in turn fed new markets: iron sections for metalwork, rails for the railways and sheet iron for the hulls of steamships. The rolling mill also brought a change from the use of a linear, alternating movement – that of a hammer – to a continuous, rotating movement in both the working and shaping of metal. This major development also took place in other industries during the same period: the saw, for instance, became circular and rotary shears replaced scissors for finishing broadcloth.

### The Quest for Continuous Production

The magnificent model of a paper-making machine displays the same *40* developments in another material. It was constructed by Eugène Philippe for the Conservatoire, which wished to keep its galleries up-to-date and show the public the most recent technological innovations. The

*40.* Model of a continuous paper-making machine with its steam-drying system, by Eugène Philippe, 1833. Inv. 4033

*39.* Machine for carding flax by Philippe de Girard (detail), 1810. Inv. 5330

*41.* Model showing a section of a blast-furnace, displaying the system for recovering gases and its application to the heating of the boiler, by Eugène Philippe, 1847. Height: 183 cm. Inv. 3082

*42.* The Martin steelworks belonging to the Compagnie des Fonderies, Forges et Aciéries in Saint-Etienne, model on a scale of 1 to 33 by Boudin, 1912. Inv. 14482

continuous paper-making machine, invented by the Frenchman Louis Nicolas Robert in 1798 and patented the following year, was perfected in England a few years later and its use spread in France during the 1820s. It used a new process, a travelling wire mesh. The machine worked continuously and linked successive processes without breaks, thus enabling savings in manpower and energy. The machine allowed the finished product, which was ready for sale after packaging, to be made more efficiently. The paper, made cheaply and in great quantity, fed the growing newspaper industry and gave rise to the development of printing ma-

43. 'Self-acting' cotton spinning-frame by Dobson and Barlow, machine-makers from Bolton. Model on a scale of 1 to 10 shown at the Universal Exhibition in London in 1862. Inv. 7175

chines such as the rotary press. This 'continuous' paper-making machine, made entirely of metal, benefited from contemporary advances in metallurgy. The wire mesh itself demonstrates the improvement in the tensile strength of metallic thread and the application of weaving techniques to metal. This sort of continuous production was soon used in glass-making and metallurgy.

### Mass Production and Industrial Society

During the second half of the 19th century a change in the scale of industrial production opened the way to mass production. In metallurgy, for instance, the prodigious rise of steel symbolised this development. Combining the qualities of cast iron (an ability to be cast and a resistance to compression) and the pliability and resistance to impact of iron, steel had been known about for a long time but its production and use had been limited by the fact that it was difficult to work with. The Bessemer process enabled steel to be obtained from a bath of molten cast iron into which air was blown to allow decarbonisation. Other methods soon emerged: Thomas, for instance, used phosphoric pig iron while Siemens-Martin used poor-quality coal and scrap-iron. Iron and steel metallurgy became the symbol of heavy industry and industrial society.

The same transition to mass production took place in textile manufacture. Mechanisation was taken as far as it could go and productivity reached a maximum. The model of a 'self-acting' spinning machine, donated to the Conservatoire by its British makers after the 1862 Universal Exhibition in London, highlights this evolution. With this invention, the worker's role was reduced to supplying and supervising the machine, which performed every single step of the manufacturing process. Alongside continually increasing mechanisation in this field, chemists and industrialists were working on the creation of artificial fibres. In 1884, Count Hilaire de Chardonnet was the first to achieve this goal with the creation of an artificial silk called rayon made from nitro-cellulose. This was soon followed by viscose, developed by two Englishmen, Cross and Bevan, before it was the turn of synthetic fibres, especially nylon, to revolutionise this field.

## From Dyes to Plastics

In 1852, confirming the essential role of textiles in nineteenth-century industry and anxious to support industrial development in France, the Conservatoire created two professorial chairs, one for teaching spinning

45. Kiln for porcelain like those used at the Minton factory, model on a scale of 1 to 5 by Digeon, 1896. Inv. 12789

44. Album of wood veneers from the West Indies and France from the firm of E. Girardot, Paris, 1882. Inv. 10246

and weaving, the other dedicated to dyeing, a closely-related field and one that was vital to the development of industrial chemistry and synthetic materials. Throughout the twentieth century, plastics have symbolised the enormous development in synthetic materials which have brought the issue of materials back into the forefront and have immediate applications in everyday life. Because of its low cost and the ease with which it could be moulded, Bakelite, a synthetic resin, invaded the car industry as well as the home: switches, radios, telephones, for example. The perfecting of polyvinyl chloride (PVC) or synthetic rubber before the Second World War, launched a new era in synthetic materials.

In the second half of the 19th century, the improvement in production techniques revolutionised the established ground-rules and gave artists new and undreamt-of resources. These opportunities also opened the way for new products which took aesthetic quality into account. With the development of production techniques, everything could be copied with unmatched perfection and new techniques could also be explored. The Conservatoire was quick to react to this issue and, in 1898, it created a chair in art applied to industry. The job was given to the architect Lucien Magne who laid the foundations of a system for teaching industrial production that combined form and function. Collections of ceramics

47. 'Coupe libellule' made of inlaid, sculpted glass by Emile Gallé, 1904, and 'paysage noir' vase after Emile Gallé, 1906. Inv. 13815 and 14031

46. Vase with blue background by Emile Gallé, 1889. Inv. 11569

48. Vases and pitcher with handle in enamelled sandstone by Jean Carriès, late 19th century. Inv. 16792/4, 7 and 2

49. Straw-coloured vase tumbler with a Venetian-style ribbon pattern and vase with a wide checked pattern from the Saint-Louis glassworks, 1853. Inv. 5981, 5978 and 5979

*50.* Two decanters and a cone-shaped vase made of rustic sandstone known as 'bronze-sandstone' from the Ziegler de Voisinlieu factory near Beauvais, 1845. Inv. 2811/8 and 11, and 3047/13

*51.* 'Nola' vase (1883) with a blue-black background, decoration in reserve and gold, and 'Chinois-Ly' vase (1849) with glazed figures in blue, both made of Sèvres porcelain. Inv. 10452 and 5226

and glass were notably improved. The works of Emile Gallé, a glass- *46, 47* blower from Lorraine, show the richness of his research: he combines existing techniques to achieve his naturalistic Art Nouveau style. As for ceramics, Carriès' stoneware revives the tradition of artistic stoneware *48* found in the Beauvais region and Chaplet's works emphasise the range *50* of research undertaken by these designers.

## Made-to-Measure Materials

Nowadays we no longer choose a material, but create one for the purpose we have in mind. Artificial materials proliferate but research is also conducted on the conventional materials whose development is de-

scribed above. The Museum displays the latest developments in traditional materials such as metal, glass, ceramics and textiles. Plastics are now used as structural components and compete with light alloys and aluminiums. They are now a key element in car manufacture. Also of importance in this domain are composite materials – a particularly good illustration of how a material can be chosen in line with its purpose – and the leading-edge biomaterials sector.

*53.* Philips loudspeaker with ebonite horn known as the 'shaving mug', and 'sonorette' radio by Sonora with Bakelite housing, *c.* 1930. Inv. 16728 / 2 and 21853

*52.* Distilling and rectifying column, in accordance with Savalle's system, model on a scale of 1 to 10, 1889. Inv. 12027

# Construction

Of all the arts and crafts, building is one of the oldest, most impressive and most popular. Surprisingly however, there is no museum specialising in the techniques used to construct the buildings that house us or the bridges that link us together. To help remedy this situation and put to good use the invaluable collections that were languishing in storerooms, one of the seven sections of the Museum has been devoted to the art of the builder.

Building was one of the trades most altered by the Industrial Revolution, and was affected by important developments which resulted from the

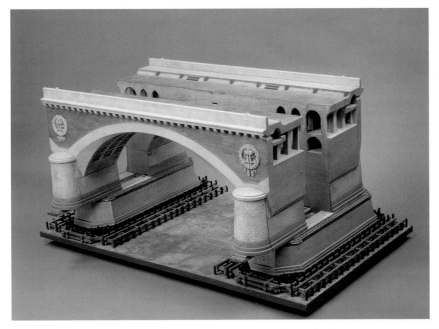

55. Model of the Pont de Pierre in Bordeaux, 1821. Height: 69 cm. Inv. 8707

advent of iron and steam. The availability of iron led to new ways of thinking about architecture, which was itself no longer based on stacking and compression but on stretching and taking into account the constraints of new materials.

## The Rules of the Art

The Pont de Pierre in Bordeaux, which still spans the Garonne, is a good 55 example of the traditional art of building, as it is depicted in great architectural encyclopaedias: it has round arches, of an average size, and is made of stone as bridges have been since Antiquity. But the model on display in the Museum has movable parts exposing the original structure, lightened by interior galleries and featuring very elaborate foundations. This collection of stones is so familiar to us today that we forget the

54. Truncated cone surrounded by barrels, for the Cherbourg dike, model on a scale of 1 to 50, c. 1885. Inv. 4114

know-how of the stonemasons who, since their predecessors the cathedral-builders, had cut their stones into very precise, geometrically exact shapes. This art was called stereotomy, and the numerous plaster models in the Museum preserve the memory of this technique. Thanks to these building-blocks resembling a children's game, craftsmen could come to the Conservatoire to learn how to cut stone according to the 'rules of the art'. Construction is the last area that can still be described as an art in the classical sense: that is, a combination of structural science and the practical knowledge of stone-cutting itself.

All aspects of the building trade are represented in the Museum, from scaffolding to hoisting techniques, particularly those developed by shipbuilders, experts in the use of wood, textiles, lifting gear and ropes. Traditional cranes, such as Brulé's – which was, incidentally, described in Diderot's *Encyclopédie* to illustrate mechanical engineering in eighteenth-century physics collections – were driven only by a treadwheel on which men walked to make the crane work. In fact, it was not very different from the crane invented at the beginning of the nineteenth century by the Parisian engineer Cavé, which was also powered by muscular strength, but had a crank and cast-iron gears making it much more efficient.

The maritime origin of lifting techniques is obvious in the models representing the pulling down, dispatching and re-erection of the Luxor obelisk in the centre of the Place de la Concorde in Paris. The models in the Museum make clear to the visitor the techniques used in these operations. Apollinaire Lebas, a marine engineer, spent four years devising and directing these spectacular operations, which culminated when the obelisk was put up in the Place de la Concorde on 25 October 1836 in front of almost two hundred thousand spectators. The meticulous models faithfully re-create the arrangement of ropes, winches and capstans which were skilfully organised so that the obelisk could be moved without difficulty. One of the models shows the ingenuity of the flat-bottomed boat built for the purpose, which was towed to Toulon by the steamship *Sphinx*.

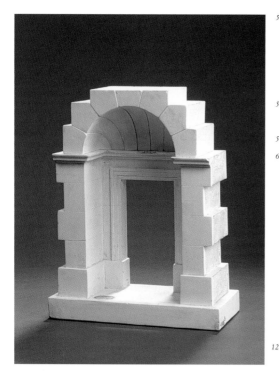

56. An example of stereotomy: arch from Saint-Antoine, late 18th century. Inv. 4108–3

## A Tradition of Large-Scale Public Works

The most grandiose human achievements have undoubtedly been linked to civil engineering works. When the English agronomist Arthur Young discovered the construction site for Cherbourg's main dike in 1788, he could hardly find words emphatic enough to express the importance of the project: 'considered in its entirety, the venture is staggering ... When this great people undertake works of capital importance, properly encouraged by the state, they find an inventive genius to draw up the plans and engineers of superior ability to execute it.' As it happens, the engineer Louis-Alexandre de Cessart was chosen by Louis XVI to build one of the most ambitious projects of the Enlightenment: a gigantic dike intended to protect Cherbourg's dock, a strategic naval base, from sea attacks and English invasion.

The project involved submerging 90 enormous boxes, shaped like truncated cones, twenty metres high and filled with stones, in order to build a dike four kilometres long. The model exhibited in the Museum, which is on a scale of 1 to 50, shows the principles adopted by Cessart for the construction of the cones and the barrels used to float them to the place they were to be submerged. In June 1786, four years after work began, the King himself chose this building-site as the destination for his first

57. Crane by Brulé, 18th century.
Height: 70 cm. Inv. 1179

58. Model of a crane by Cavé, on a scale of
1 to 5, by Pierre Clair, c. 1840. Height: 93 cm.
Inv. 2703

journey outside the Ile de France. But this memorable event and the perseverance of everybody involved in the project were not enough to overcome the many obstacles encountered. Only 18 cones were sunk between 1784 and 1788, the project came to a premature end and the job was finished in a more conventional fashion.

61 Charles Couvreux's models of a dredger and excavator, on the other hand, bear witness to the memorable success of one large nineteenth-century building-site: the construction of the Suez Canal. From the time it was imagined in the eighteenth century, to the studies made during the expedition to Egypt, to the official opening by the Empress Eugénie

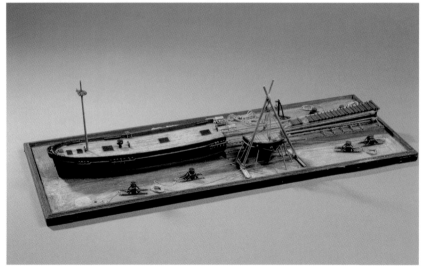

59. Model of the device used by Lebas to dismantle the Luxor obelisk. Inv. 17848–1

60. Model of the device used by Lebas to load the Luxor obelisk onto the boat. Inv. 17848–2

on 17 November 1869, it took almost a century to give birth to one of the greatest technical wagers of all time. The Suez Canal owes its existence to the perseverance of two men, Saïd Pasha and Ferdinand de Lesseps. The latter's name is still remembered, but the industrialists, inventors and contractors who managed the project were soon forgotten, as often happens. Yet the building-site for this gigantic canal linking the Mediterranean to the Red Sea was the largest excavation of the nineteenth century. Almost ninety dredgers dug out the route of the canal. But the task proved titanic, and huge dredgers and excavators had to be built to speed up the digging. The digging machines custom-built by the Couvreux firm moved along the canal bank on railway tracks and emptied the rubble into special trains. These excavating machines were very advanced

61. Model of Charles Couvreux's dredger, with a conveyor-belt to transport the rubble. Height: 1.15 m. Inv. 11931

*62–63.* Scale model of the construction of a building on the rue de Rivoli in Paris, on a scale of 1 to 20, by Desplanques, 1879. Inv. 9504

# Communication

To attain the goal of exchanging information as fast as possible all over the world, technical methods of recording, transmitting and processing data have multiplied, as has the amount of data. The hegemony of the written and printed word, the distribution of which was limited by the speed of terrestrial transport, was succeeded by electromechanical and then electronic techniques, while the visual techniques of photography and cinema opened the door to artistic creation. The progressive development of these methods dictated the setting-up, organisation and control of increasingly extensive terrestrial and spatial networks. There are political, cultural and economic aspects at stake here: the exchange of a growing amount of information is rapidly and profoundly changing the way societies evolve. Under the generic term 'communication' the Museum presents the gradual proliferation of methods of communication, the origins of each one, and its earliest technical developments.

## The Age of Printing

The world changed with the invention of printing, traditionally associated with the name of Gutenberg. Between 1430 and 1450 the reproduction of texts using movable metal type and a hand-press was perfected, and led to the earliest distribution of printed books. This major innovation meant that texts could be reproduced rapidly and in quantity and that the price of books could be lowered because production costs were split between several copies. By 1500 the printed book had conquered Europe and established itself as the dominant medium for four centuries, reaching its apotheosis during the Enlightenment. The hand-press with movable type symbolised this important change which took place in Renaissance and Reformation Europe, a period characterised by the ferment of ideas taking place. The hand-press, which was built mainly of wood and had two strong uprights and a powerful screw, enabled workers to print around three thousand sheets a day! However, the spread of printed material was still limited to a rich and enlightened minority because of the low levels of literacy and the restricted output of these workshops. The number of copies in each print-run remained low and the works were disseminated by booksellers and master printers. The whole system represented 'Ancien Régime typography', which was to prevail 68 from the sixteenth to the eighteenth century.

The model of a printing press displayed here, with its metal screw, is evi- 67 dence of the work carried out in the eighteenth century in an attempt to improve this rustic instrument and particularly the evenness of the pressure applied. This development was more than just a matter of production techniques and its effects were not simply quantitative: new types of

68. Portable printing-press owned by Pajot, Count of Ons-en-Bray, 1734. Inv. 518

67. Model of a typographic hand-press, 18th century. Height: 85 cm. Inv. 12124

books and readers were appearing, as were distribution networks and new ways of reading. All of which showed the new role played by printed works during the Enlightenment and foreshadowed its transition to the status of an industry in the following century.

In 1810, to meet the increased demand which had first emerged in the second half of the eighteenth century, and benefiting from improvements in materials and progress in mechanical engineering, Koenig and Bauer succeeded in mechanising the printing press. Their press, like the paper-making machine invented a few years earlier, used the rotary principle, thus ensuring that printing could take place at great speed. As a result, printers would be able to respond to the newspapers' desire to expand and their demand that papers be printed more quickly. Once again,

69. Small-scale model of Gaveaux's press with two cylinders and two margin devices, c. 1845. Inv. 13761.
*Opposite:* detail

the mechanisation process called into question the way the book trade was organised in general. The need to see a return on considerable investments required bigger print-runs and compelled editors and booksellers to think about the content and form of books and reorganise their distribution, in a period which also saw the development of rapid forms of transport, especially railways. Gaveaux's model of the printing press testifies to this progress. Built entirely of metal by a Parisian expert, it enabled two pages to be printed with each passage of the bed and meant that tens of thousands of pages could be printed every day.

During the same period, man fulfilled one of the dreams of his ancestors: capturing an image and fixing it on a support. Photography found its earliest form in the discoveries of Niepce and Daguerre and began to spread after 1840. Using a complex procedure, the image was printed onto a copper plate covered with a layer of silver and sensitised with an iodide emulsion before being exposed inside a camera. Charles Chevallier's *Great Photographer,* which shows him alongside all his equipment and chemicals, implies that behind the technical and aesthetic qualities of photography lies a complex series of processes, requiring that the early photographers be talented chemists too. Despite the lengthy exposure time and the complexity of the development process, the daguerreotype was a great success. Landscapes, scientific images and, above all, portraits turned photography into an artistic activity.

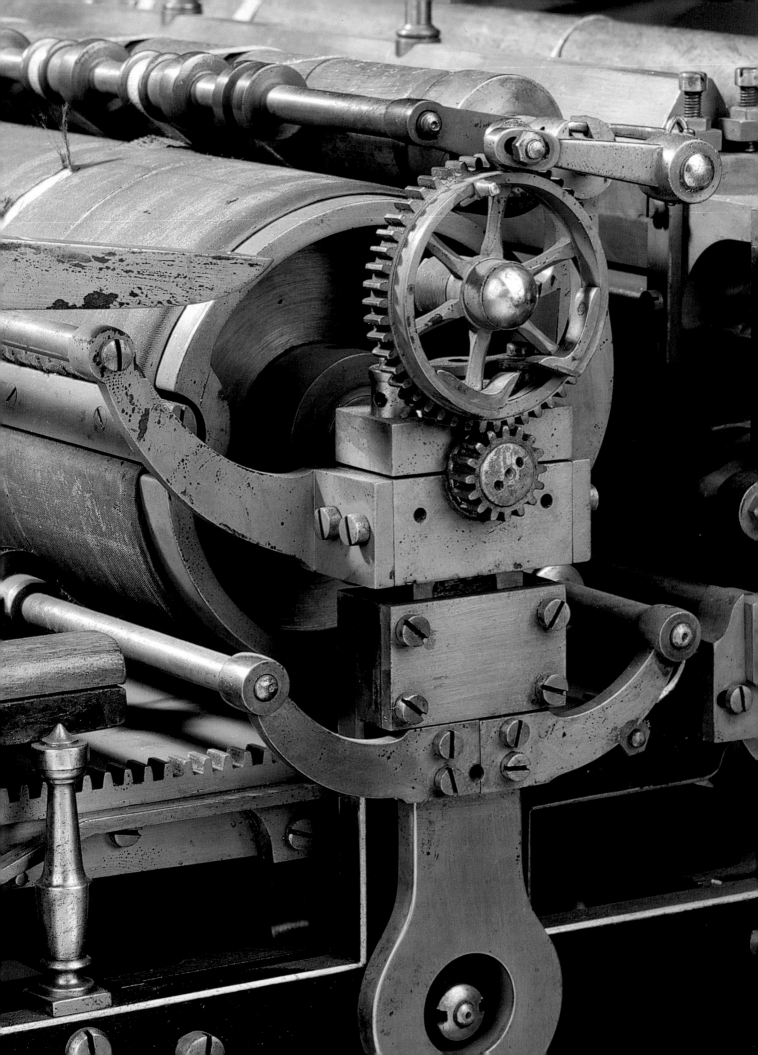

## The Birth of the Telegraph

On 30 August 1794, less than an hour after the event, a still famous message announced the recapture of Condé-sur-Escaut by Republican troops and thus confirmed the position of the Committee of Public Safety. This was the first successful application of the optical telegraph invented by Chappe, introduced in France two years earlier. Leaving drum-beats and smoke signals far behind, this was the first complete communications network. Its development and uses already demonstrated the vital features of modern communication: speed of transmis-

70. *The Great Photographer,* the optician Charles Chevallier's dark room, with his accessories, 1841. Inv. 6874

71. Model of Chappe's telegraph, early 19th century. Inv. 14601

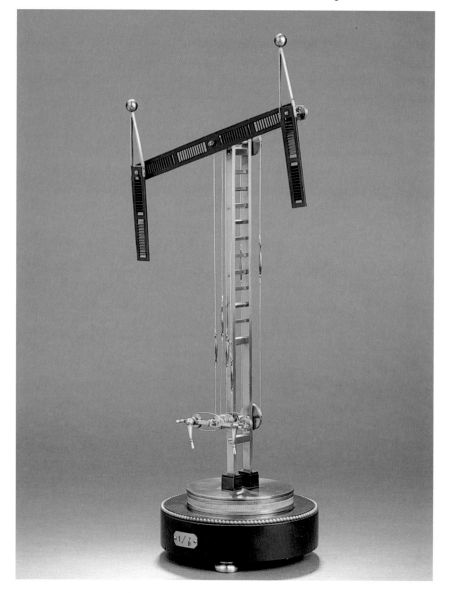

sion, continuity and permanent availability of the network, control of information and a qualified staff. The network was made up of a series of towers, all of which were topped with transmitters made up of three articulated arms. The successive positions of these arms constituted words which the man stationed at each post observed with a telescope on the previous transmitter before passing it on to the following one. The confidential nature of the messages and the need for the system to work fast required the creation of a code. But the maintenance costs in terms of materials and men and the disruption caused by bad weather restricted the spread of the network and limited its use.

By around 1837, thanks to increasing knowledge of electricity and the

*72.* 'Collection of fossils and shells',
daguerreotype by Louis Jacques Mandé
Daguerre, 1839. Inv. 8745/2

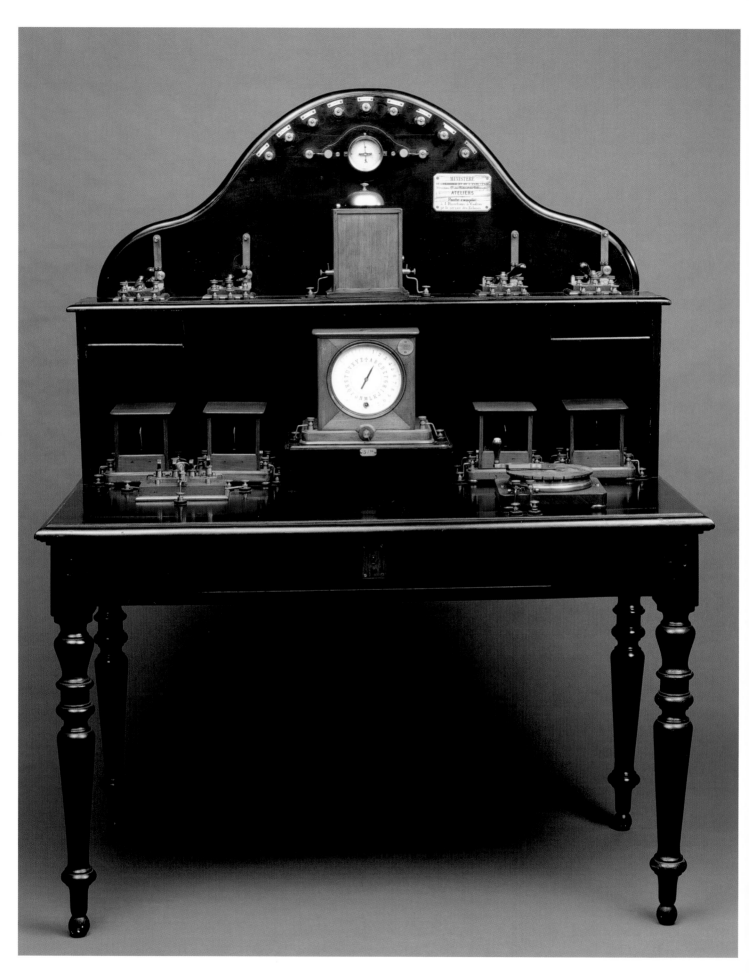

70

development of reliable batteries and electromagnets, it became possible to transmit messages over long distances. The first electric telegraph line was opened in 1839 by two Englishmen, Cook and Wheatstone, backed by a railway company. The device, a transmitter and receiver in one, featured the alphabet and two magnetic needles which pointed towards each of the letters indicated by the electrical impulses from the transmitter, thereby reconstructing the message letter by letter. Because of the speed of transmission and the reliability of the electric telegraph, railway companies were quick to adopt it to make sure that their trains were being run properly and safely.

The success of the Morse code after 1845 ensured the development of the network by guaranteeing the security of transmissions and the printing of messages. Official communications, stock-exchange rates, railway information and soon press releases became the main uses of the network, which developed quickly in the second half of the nineteenth century. The completion of the first transatlantic cable in 1866 consolidated the importance of the telegraph, which by then had developed into a global network. A few years later, it became possible to send several messages *73* simultaneously on the same line, thus expanding the telegraph's capacity all over the world and eliminating time and distance.

## The Golden Age of the Press

Throughout the nineteenth century, periodicals and newspapers were a driving force in printed matter and the end of the century was to be their golden age. In France it all began under the July Monarchy, which saw the emergence of mass-market newspapers continually striving to increase their print-runs and lower their prices and manufacturing costs, in an attempt to win the largest possible circulation. The technical developments of this period are symbolised by the rotary press. In 1883, in a significant gesture also aimed at establishing its reputation, Marinoni, the best-known French manufacturer of printing machines, gave the Conservatoire a rotary press with its own cutting and binding machine. *74* Intended for the *Petit Journal,* one of the most important daily newspapers in Paris in the late nineteenth century, it was capable of producing twenty thousand copies an hour. To match the capacity and speed of these machines, typesetting became mechanised in its turn and Linotype was first used in the USA in 1884, confirming the young nation as a major player in the field of communications, as it was in many other areas.

The zenith of mass-market newspapers was during the Belle Epoque when they recorded public opinion and political life. Zola's celebrated open letter, *J'accuse,* is still the most famous symbol of this. The press was already the instigator behind sporting and media events. In 1908, it was the British *Daily Mail* that came up with the idea of giving a prize of 25,000 francs to the first pilot who managed to cross the Channel. After Louis Blériot's success, the Parisian daily paper *Le Matin* covered the *9* event and bought the plane, which was exhibited in front of its offices before being donated to the Conservatoire.

## From Photography for Everybody to the Cinema

The development and commercialisation in the 1870s of a gelatino-silver bromide emulsion revitalised photography. This substance, together with progress made in optics such as the development of the shutter,

*74.* Rotary printing press by Marinoni (detail), 1883. Inv. 10733

*73.* Complete electric telegraph set, with four directions on the dial, used by lock-keepers, 1880. Inv. 14668

finally made it possible to take snapshots and manufacture hand-held, or 'tourist', cameras, some of which had several plates. This simplification was the first step in the popularisation of photography, and from this point on the exposure time gradually decreased from a few minutes to a fraction of a second. Beginners were offered all sorts of practical and easy-to-use cameras. They took other forms, such as the many small *75* 'spy' cameras in the Museum (the *Escopette,* or blunderbuss, by Darier, is a good example). The decisive step in the popularisation of the camera was Eastman's marketing in 1889 of the Kodak camera, a simple and cheap camera with flexible roll-film on a celluloid base.

*75.* Bellows and changing frame-feed magazine by Balbreck, 1890 and the *Escopette,* or 'blunderbuss' camera by Darier, 1889. Inv. 16373 and 16484

*76* The Lumière brothers' camera and their famous projection at the Grand Café in 1895, marked the advent of the cinema. The idea had been in the air and many scientists were working on analysing and reproducing *77* movement, among them Emile Reynaud with his praxinoscope and the physiologist Etienne-Jules Marey with his chronophotography. Its success was ensured by the use of flexible film, and a system that enabled it to be unrolled intermittently, combined with projection on a large screen. Very soon the cinema found its own language, that of the seventh art, with its own repertoire, narrative and codes, and established itself as an artistic medium, while making and distributing the films soon required the industrial methods used by the great studios.

## Reproducing and Transmitting the Voice

In 1877, Thomas Edison captured and reproduced the human voice on *78* his gramophone, succeeding where many others had failed. A metal stylus impressed a groove onto a tin sheet; the depth of the groove was determined by the movements of the microphone that picked up the sound waves emitted by the voice. As the stylus ran along the tin cylinder, it transmitted the vibrations to the speaker which reproduced the sound. The tin cylinders were soon replaced by wax ones and then by resin discs, while galvanoplasty allowed master copies to be made and thus enabled mass production. Here again, the use of electricity and of synthetic materials – vinyl – marked a considerable step forward, emphasising the constant interaction between the various areas of technical science.

76. Reversible camera known as the
*cinématographe,* by Louis and Auguste
Lumière, built by Charles Moisson, 1895.
Gift from Louis Lumière. Inv. 16966

77. Emile Reynaud's stereoscopic binocular
praxinoscope, 1902. Inv. 16554

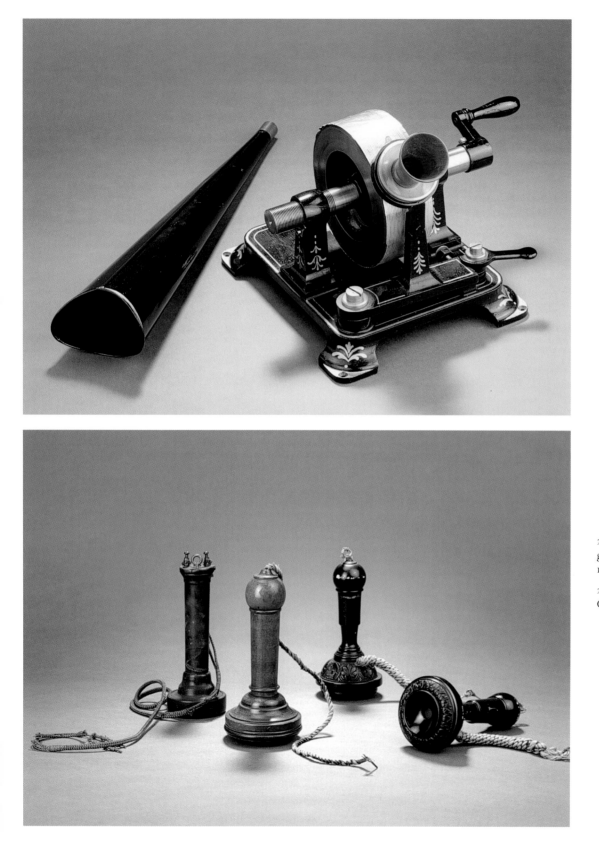

78. Thomas Edison's gramophone with tin sheet, 1877. Inv. 20435

79. Telephones by Alexander Graham Bell, 1877. Inv. 16081

In the USA in 1876, Alexander Graham Bell and Elisha Gray invented the telephone. The principle had been known but had not yet been put into 79 practice since there was no demand for it and there was competition from the telegraph. As well as the technical achievement it represented, made possible by an all-important knowledge of electromagnetism, the telephone offered hitherto unexplored possibilities: instantaneous communication at a distance with neither a special code nor a written message, and the ability to work simultaneously in both directions. The telephone opened the way for individual, verbal relationships and filled the need that the telegraph had been unable to satisfy for private, urban communications. The major contribution of the telephone lay in the change in social behaviour that it brought about, and its success results from its use, unforeseen by those who promoted it, for private conversations. The series of telephones exhibited in the Museum shows the profusion of manufacturers who were involved before the state decided to standardise the models, and also highlights the telephone's quality as a domestic object that had to fit into homes and offices. The telephone network soon dominated communication.

## Radio and Television, the Rise of the Mass Media

The arrival of the radio and the use of magnetic waves to transmit information was again the result of research by several scientists and can be described as a collective achievement. In 1890, Edouard Branly developed his *coherer*, the first device able to detect and receive waves, but it 80 was Marconi who made the first successful radiotelegraphic link. The new medium, wireless telegraphy, eliminated the need for the equipment previously used and gave rise to new possibilities. In competition with the telegraph, which was firmly established all over the world, the radio was first used for communications between people on the move and in areas where communication by telephone proved impossible or too expensive. At first Morse code was used and the first major application of the radio was to communicate with ships at sea. On 14 April 1912, radio distress signals sent by the *Titanic* enabled eight hundred people to be rescued thanks to the prompt arrival of another vessel.

However, radio made significant progress only with the use of electronic components, in particular, the tubes which made it possible to amplify an electronic current. The triode patented by Lee De Forest in 1907, first used as a receiver and amplifier, was later used as a transmitter, increasing the potential of radio which was now capable of accurately broadcasting voices and music. The radio became a true mass medium, addressing thousands of listeners, altering ways of life and establishing a privileged link with the public by means of its broadcast of regular programmes. Broadcasting created new jobs and its own language. The number of stations multiplied, particularly in the USA, and laid the foundations for our communications-based society.

In the nineteenth century, research was conducted on the long-distance transmission of images. In 1860, the priest Giovanni Caselli, with the help of the famous instrument-maker Froment, developed his amazing *pantelegraph,* which enabled static images to be transmitted between Paris and Lyon. At the beginning of the twentieth century, Edouard Belin encountered great success with his *belinograph,* which was used by journalists. But the transmission of moving images had to wait until after World War One, when electronic components were developed.

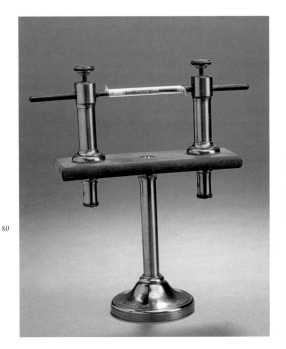

80. Edouard Branly's *coherer,* 1890. Inv. 16132

*81.* '30-line' television receiver by
René Barthélémy, 1931. Inv. 20252

Electromechanical scanning, first studied by the Scot John Logie Baird, gave way to electronic systems. The analysis of the moving image was extremely complex and it was not until 1929, in the USA, that Zworykin developed the 'iconoscope', the first tube that could be used to analyse and reproduce the moving image. In France, the engineer René Barthé- 81 lémy carried out his research at the Compagnie Française des Comp-

82. Memory with ferrite core, element from the memory of an IBM 7030 'Stretch' computer, 1959. Inv. 22480/3

teurs and organised the first television experiment on 14 April 1931. Four years later, the first television network opened in Paris for the privileged few. It was just after the war that television expanded in earnest. New ways of analysing images, an improvement in the definition of the picture and an increase in the number of transmitters ensured its spread. Television, along with radio, became a mass medium, entered into people's homes, and profoundly changed the social fabric and family life.

## From the Analogue System to the Digital System

With the approach of the twenty-first century, techniques of communication and the mass media have a central place – and one of increasing economic importance – in contemporary societies and they are expanding rapidly across the world. Historical borders between different sectors have become blurred. Since the last war, progress in electronic components – transistors, integrated circuits and microprocessors – have led 82 the way to miniaturisation and increased power. But the most important development was in the field of information technology, initially confined to telecommunications, but which went on to affect all methods of communication, with digitisation as its symbol. Nowadays, it is no longer sounds, words, static or moving images that are being transmitted, but rather digital data dispatched across worldwide networks like the Internet, or distributed in the form of multi-media products such as CD-ROMs.

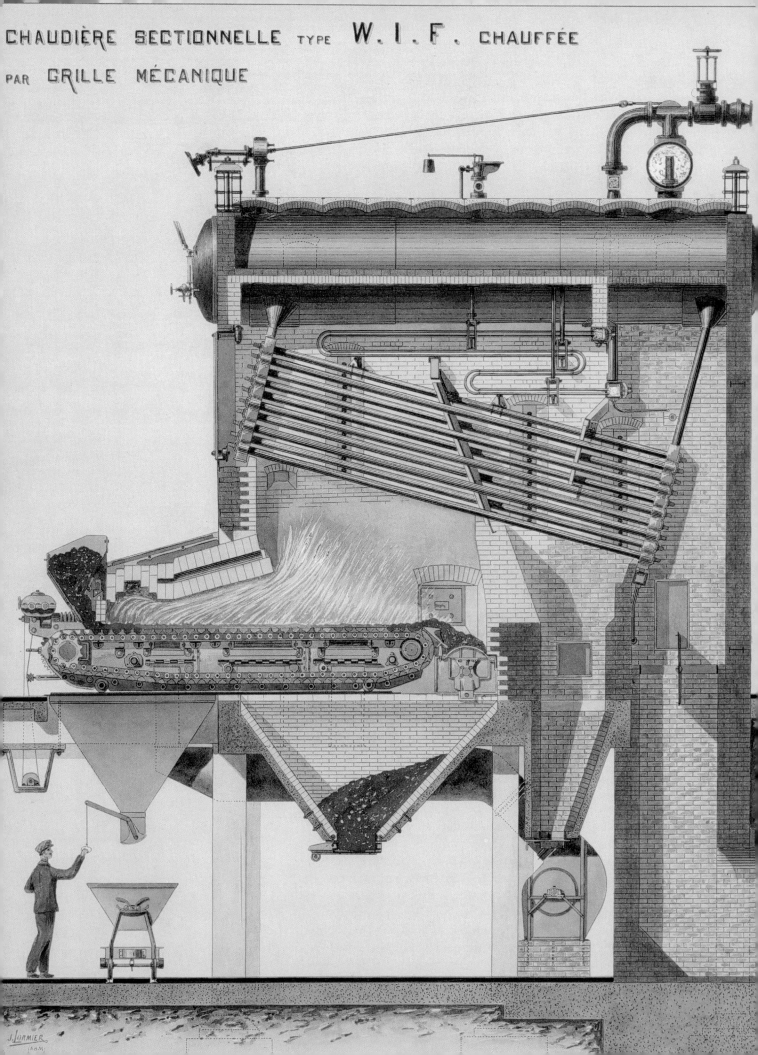

CHAUDIÈRE SECTIONNELLE TYPE W.I.F. CHAUFFÉE
PAR GRILLE MÉCANIQUE

# Energy

All the major technical innovations of modern times have been distinguished by significant progress in the field of energy: mills in the Middle Ages, steam engines in the eighteenth century and electricity at the end of the nineteenth century. The last example plays such a fundamental role in our society that it is almost impossible to imagine a civilisation deprived of this omnipresent source of power. But if we take a closer look, we will see that a significant proportion of the electricity used in the world is still of hydraulic origin. Techniques have certainly improved, but the turbines in big modern power-stations are not very dif-

84. Horizontal hydraulic wheel from Kabylia. Height: 1.13 m. Inv. 21231

ferent from the first hydraulic wheels which, as in Kabylia (Algeria), rotated on their vertical axis and worked the millstone, thus providing food for the family.

By means of the numerous engines exhibited and preserved there, the Musée des arts et métiers retraces the history of how energy was harnessed, and particularly the research that led, for example, to windmills. A beautiful wooden model on a scale of one to ten faithfully reproduces a large windmill installed in the arsenal at Rochefort in 1806. This very innovative mill worked a winch which towed a small boat equipped with a dredger used to clear mud from the gates of the dry-dock in which ships were built. This very unusual combination once again illustrates the primary function of the Conservatoire, that is, to acquaint the public with the most recent innovations. Furthermore, despite the imposing size of the mill, its upper section could turn on its axis to align the sails so that they caught the wind. This turning-point in the nineteenth century

83. Drawing of a Babcock Wilcox sectional boiler, watercolour, early 20th century. Inv. TG 461

*86.* Model of the Marly machine,
18th century. Height: 1.14 m. Inv. 173

*85.* Windmill with revolving upper section,
model on a scale of 1 to 10, 1806. Inv. 4074

marks the apotheosis of the techniques which originated in the Middle Ages and the Renaissance, and the mill displays these highly skilled craftsmen's absolute mastery of carpentry.

For a long time, builders from Northern Europe were authorities in the art of building mills, and particularly machines for draining water, and so it was natural for Louis XIV to call on Renkin Sualem (1645–1708), from Liège, to build the monumental Marly machine which supplied the fountains in the gardens at Versailles. Between 1681 and 1688 about 1,800 men worked on this gigantic structure, with its 14 hydraulic wheels which worked about 250 pumps to bring the water 162 metres above the level of the Seine. The exquisite model in the Musée des arts et métiers, made in the eighteenth century, reproduces only one part of the mechanism, to

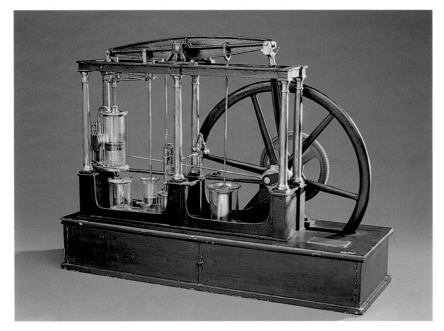

88. James Watt's steam engine, demonstration model by Clair, early 19th century. Height: 64 cm. Inv. 5094–1

show visitors to the Conservatoire the techniques used for driving a machine before the industrial era. The noisy clamour of the rods can no longer be heard, but the complexity of the model gives an inkling of the trouble the engineers at Versailles charged with the machine's maintenance must have had.

## Engines in the Industrial Revolution

Made mainly of wood, the Marly machine is a remarkable example of pre-industrial techniques, relegated to status as an antique when the nascent Industrial Revolution introduced a new energy, steam, and a new material, iron, more solid and less cumbersome than wood.

The first 'fire engines' – the earliest steam engines – were used in mines in Cornwall to drain water from the floors of the galleries. In 1698, the military engineer Thomas Savery (1650–1715) patented a machine able to pump water 'by means of the propelling force of fire'. Soon after fruitless trials by Denis Papin, Savery's 'fire engine' became the first steam engine used in the industrial world.

The 'miner's friend', as its inventor called it, had no piston and applied the principle of the vacuum created by the condensation of steam to suck up water from the bottom of the mine and return it to the surface using a system of taps and valves. To illustrate its complex operation, Nollet had a small demonstration model made in the best tradition of

87. Model of Savery's fire engine from Nollet's collection, late 18th century. Height: 84 cm. Inv. 4409

the machines in his famous collection. Through the use of glass cylinders and clearly visible mechanism, the machine explains the ingenious principle of sucking up water by means of the vacuum created by steam and its evaporation.

Still rudimentary at the beginning of the eighteenth century, the steam engine was considerably improved throughout the century and established itself as the real driving force of the Industrial Revolution with the 88 steam engine developed by James Watt (1736–1819). One of the models in the Museum, which now has an electric motor, demonstrates the working of the new engine developed by the Scottish engineer around 1781. We can see how the monumental beam transfers the power, which originates in the steam cylinder, to the great cast-iron fly-wheel which soon

89. Lenoir's gas engine, 1861. Inv. 7652

replaced the paddle wheel in new factories, thus freeing industrialists from seasonal constraints relating to the height of water in rivers.

Although already very advanced, with its governor, automatic functioning and indispensable steam boiler, Watt's engine was still far too heavy and bulky to be used for anything apart from driving machines in workshops. However, British engineers, who often came from families of mill-builders, addressed this problem and converted Watt's static engine into a locomotive, thus opening the way for the railway age which began in the late 1820s. There was still a long way to go before these engines could be put in road vehicles and for many years steam engines were 90 only used for working machines in paper-mills and textile factories.

### An Engine for the Road

Another giant advance was required to escape from the constraints of the steam boiler, which was not only dangerous but consumed huge amounts of wood and coal too. The self-taught mechanical engineer Jean-Joseph-Etienne Lenoir (1822–1900), who came from Luxembourg, 89 invented the first internal-combustion engine. Though similar in many ways to a steam engine, Lenoir's engine did not have a boiler. Combustion no longer took place outside the engine but in the cylinder itself, in which gas, used as a fuel, was ignited by a spark-plug similar to the ones found in modern cars. Many engineers before Lenoir had tried to eliminate the use of steam and to go directly from thermal to mechanical

*90.* Model of a locomobile which can travel by
road, 19th century. Height: 38 cm. Inv. 16694

91. Dynamo-electric machine by Gramme,
c. 1880. Height: 54 cm. Inv. 9649–1

92. Single-cylinder engine by De Dion and
Bouton, 1899. Inv. 13170

energy, but no one had yet been successful. The engine was still unwieldy and not very powerful, but it was a step forward, and it took only about thirty years for the technique to be refined and for smaller and lighter but more powerful engines to be developed.

One of the most extraordinary of these is the single-cylinder engine developed in 1889 by the Marquis of Dion and the mechanical engineer Georges Bouton. This small engine which ran on oil had 1.5 horsepower (i.e. about 1100 watts) for a mass of only 25 kilograms, which meant that it was immediately used to propel airships. From the airship to the aeroplane, from the aeroplane to the tricycle, then to the motor-car, the internal-combustion engine developed very quickly.

In the space of only a few years, the golden age of the motor-car natu-

93. Alessandro Volta's Voltaic pile (battery), 1800. Height: 71 cm. Inv. 1701

rally brought to an end that of the steam engine. At the turn of the century, new and bold engineers took to the skies with ingenious engines using a rotary action which truly launched the conquest of space. Gnome engines – such as the Gnome Delta of 1912 which had nine cylinders and was invented by the Seguin brothers, members of a family of engineers who had become famous for building suspension bridges and railways during the nineteenth century – made a name for themselves in World War One, on both banks of the Rhine.

One final twentieth-century energy source remains: electricity. In the 1870s, after decades of trial and error, several physicists, such as Gramme, Pacinotti and Froment, succeeded in taming this impalpable energy.

### The Advent of Electrical Machines

Electricity in itself was not a novelty in the second half of the nineteenth century. Experiments using static electricity – the electric kiss, sparkling candles and jumping puppets – had featured in the physics collections of the previous century. But no sooner had it been created than electricity disappeared in a trail of sparks because nobody knew how to control or preserve it. The Italian Alessandro Volta (1745–1827) made his name when he was granted a pension by Napoleon in 1801 for developing the first battery. This major development enabled electricity to be produced from a basic chemical reaction. But, however important this first step

may have been, no one yet imagined using it for industrial purposes. Everything was explained much later when the theoretical basis of electricity was understood. This was a far cry from what had happened with the steam engine, which came long before the theory of thermodynamics. Gramme's dynamo, on the other hand, owed much to the physicists *91* of the nineteenth century. This reversible machine enabled electricity to create mechanical energy and vice-versa, and was extensively used in workshops and in new electricity grids. Of course, it was many more years before electricity was used in the home. But the most flexible energy ever imagined was now available.

A new world began with the new century. Once the engines had been invented and the infrastructure set up, a new age was born: the consumer age. Coal and oil had been exploited to the point where supplies were almost exhausted when countries decided to move in two complementary directions: nuclear energy, on the one hand, involved the use of uranium, a new fuel which was available in quantity and was, all things considered, economical; on the other hand, there was a move towards the more rational management of resources and the use of renewable forms of energy. This development, which has been viewed as an absolute necessity since the two oil crises of the Seventies, is now one of the key concerns of responsible politicians, industrialists and, increasingly, citizens. The Museum presents these two routes as the final important development in this section, with scale models of a nuclear power-station, a wind turbine and a 'green' house. The age of all-out consumption will be followed by the age of reason, with the recognition that we cannot leave the generations to come with a planet stripped of its energy resources. This humanist planetary vision, which not long ago was shared only by a few idealists, is on the way to becoming the creed of the most industrialised nations in the coming century.

*94.* Gnome Delta rotary engine with nine cylinders, 1912. Inv. 14594

# Mechanics

Mechanics is, above all, the subject that takes us back to our origins, to the mechanists and automaton-makers of classical Greece and to the machines that have invaded our daily lives in the last two centuries. Mechanics, the key discipline in the Musée des arts et métiers, has had an important place here since the very start with the famous machines left to Louis XVI by Jacques Vaucanson. While industrial mechanisation was developing, mechanics 'applied to the arts' was one of the first three professorial chairs created at the Conservatoire in 1819. Following in this tradition, the Museum exhibits not only the basic components and elementary mechanisms in this field, but also its principal applications and industrial and domestic machines.

At the beginning of the eighteenth century, the fundamental principles of mechanics were established on the basis of rules dating back to Antiquity. To these basic principles, such as levers and inclined planes, were added gears, cams, the crank-arm system, pulleys, hoists and so on. Research intensified and mechanists managed, for example, to reduce the effects of friction on gears by improving the shape of the cogs and their teeth. By the end of the seventeenth century, Hooke had developed a helical cog, and then La Hire had studied the epicycloidal shape of the teeth of the cogs. This research was quickly applied to clockmaking and in other areas of mechanics.

This theoretical work on the design of gears contrasts with how they were actually used in most pre-industrial machines. The models in the Museum show the preponderance of simple mechanisms such as camshafts and levers, as well as the use of a system known as the trundle-gear. Built mainly of wood and used in mills, such as the one in 85 Rochefort, it was fairly basic, losing much of its force through friction. But it has survived thanks to its simplicity, low cost and its ability to be repaired on the spot.

## Clockmaking: a Leading-edge Sector

The evolution of clockmaking was very important in the development of mechanics during the Enlightenment. To satisfy the need to measure time ever more precisely, clockmakers invented their own tools and devised small machine-tools to enable them to execute with precision the most delicate and repetitive operations: machines for cutting cogs and shaping their teeth; small lathes to sharpen cogs and spindles. Clockmaking consistently took the lead in technical matters and controlled the general development of applied mechanics. But it was also the first industry to apply the theoretical knowledge of physics and mechanics.

The Museum has on display a series of small machines made by the most

Detail of the iron lathe attributed to Desbordes, see fig. 97, p. 93

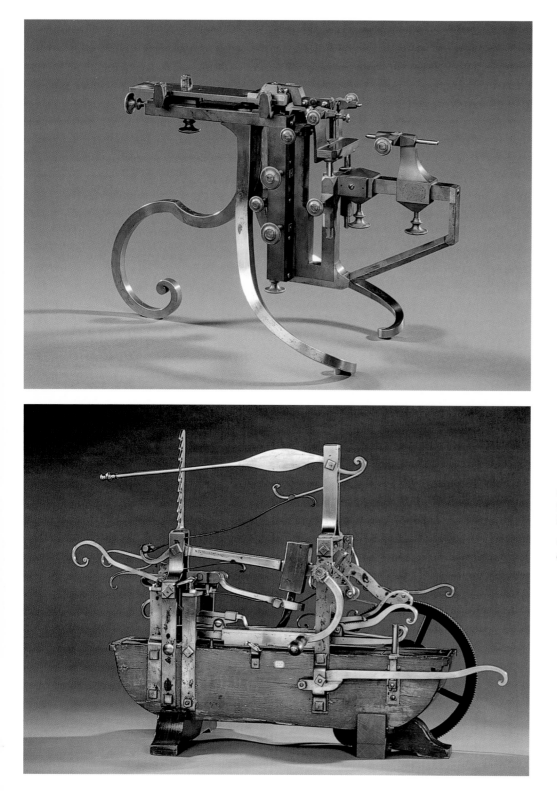

95. Machine for rounding off
the teeth of cog-wheels, made by
Samuel Gautier, 1766. Inv. 1351

96. Machine for sharpening files,
c. 1750. Inv. 4162

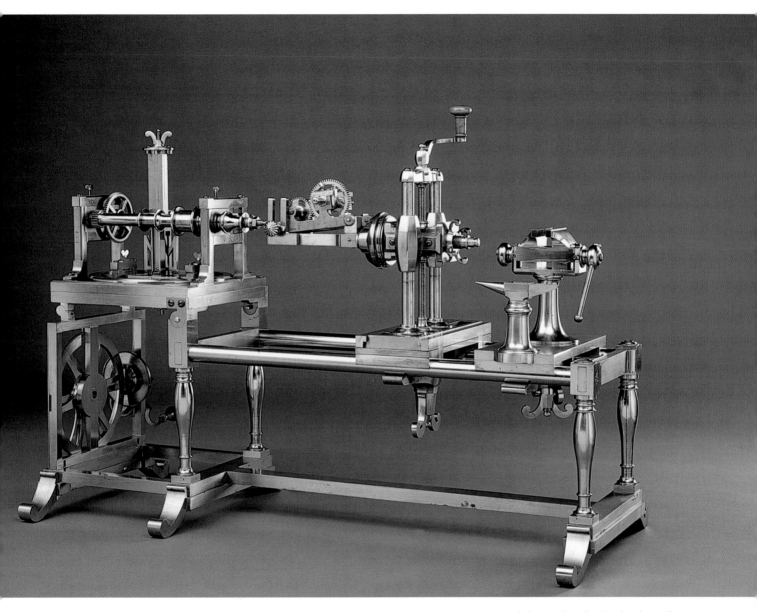

97. Iron lathe attributed to Desbordes with
a small vice and a two-horned anvil mounted
on a wagon on runners, carriage and support,
mid-18th century. Inv. 1101

important clockmakers and mechanists of the eighteenth century, such as Thiout, Hulot, Jacob Droz and Ferdinand Berthoud. The machine for rounding off cog-wheels made by Samuel Gautier in 1766 is a representative example of these small machines which combine inventiveness and craftsmanship with a stylish appearance. Dating from the same period, the extraordinary machine for sharpening files bears witness to the research conducted by clockmakers with a view to making these many indispensable tools. In this piece, too, the maker combined aesthetics and functionality, transforming all the levers and clamping-screws into the legs and wings of a fantastic insect.

### A Machine for Making Machines

The lathe, a basic machine-tool, was the founding machine of industrial mechanics. At the beginning of the eighteenth century it was employed as it had always been to fashion wood and iron. Only the small lathes used by clockmakers were made of metal at this point, and they were improved in significant ways, particularly in the method of guiding the tools. The most

98. Oil painting on canvas of a man in front of a rose engine, 18th century. Inv. 14742

99. Rose engine belonging to King Louis XVI (detail), made by Mercklein in 1780. Inv. 114

striking change was the move to using metal for large lathes which in turn enabled large parts for industrial machines – mainly steam engines – to be built with precision and consistency. The slide lathe built in 1751 by Vaucanson, an exceptional piece and the symbol of this development, was made entirely of metal and was equipped with a system of prismatic guides for the chuck-carriage.

But the 'art of turning', which spread thanks to numerous manuals in the eighteenth century, was also an exercise in virtuosity and a much-loved pastime in high society. At the end of the eighteenth century, lathes

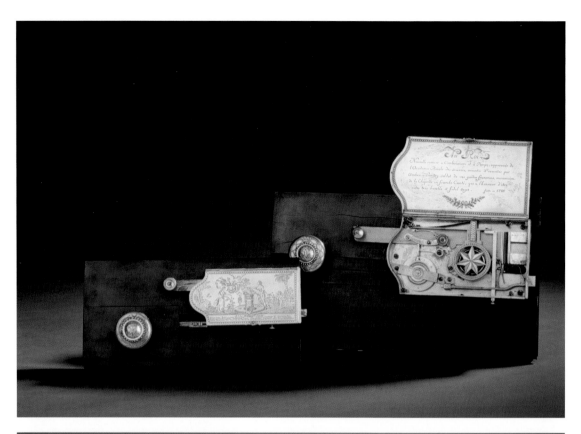

were often found in curiosity cabinets or were owned by members of the nobility: these people were following an example from on high, since Louis XVI had himself taken up this activity. His rose engine, made by the mechanical engineer Mercklein around 1785, highlights the exquisite quality of these machines, which were used to apply an infinite variety of geometric decorations to tobacco and jewellery boxes and, in particular, watch-cases. Combining inventiveness and rigour, creativity and manual dexterity, the pieces made by the virtuoso turner François Barreau help us to understand the passion for this art during the Enlightenment.

*99*

*101*

## Vaucanson, an Ingenious Mechanist

The figure of Jacques Vaucanson (1709–1782), who dominated mechanical engineering in the eighteenth century, perfectly illustrates the numerous developments in this field. In 1738 his three automata established him as one of the leading mechanical engineers, but also marked an important stage in the study of artificial man, backed by mechanistic philosophy. A few years later Vaucanson, like the clockmakers, made tools and ma-

chine-tools which contributed to the development of industrial machines. The sliding lathe mentioned above enabled the improvement of the rollers used to calender cloth. While inventing a chain to improve the transmission of movement, he also devised a machine to make the chain. Finally, asked by the state to try to improve the silk industry and appointed as a factory inspector, he introduced significant innovations in organzine mills and in the automation of weaving. He also helped spread technical progress by setting up model factories, and attempted to improve the whole production system by means of mechanisation.

*102*

## The Automaton Theatre

During his or her visit to the Mechanics section, the visitor discovers, as if opening a jewellery box, the splendid collection of androids, automata, mechanical musical instruments, musical clocks and mechanical toys belonging to the Musée des arts et métiers. Mechanists used all their skill and inventiveness to place their talents at the service of fantasy and fascination.

*102.* Chain-making machine by Vaucanson, built by Rosa, *c.* 1750. Inv. 6

*100.* Combination and spring locks dedicated to Louis XVI and Marie-Antoinette, made by Poux-Landry, 1787. Inv. 937/1 and 2

*101.* Turned pieces of wood and ivory, made by François Barreau, late 18th century. Inv. 104

97

Since Antiquity, man has searched relentlessly for ways of reproducing the movements of humans or animals. The automata made by the mechanists of Alexandria inspired their successors in the Renaissance, designers of hydraulic fountains for princely gardens, of musical instruments and singing birds. The eighteenth century was undeniably the golden age for automata but it drew its inspiration from this tradition. The Museum owns a delightful collection of pieces from this period demonstrating the creativity of the makers and the diversity of the pieces, which combine automata, mechanical musical instruments and clockmaking.

*103*

The most talented designers attempted to achieve a perfect reproduction of the main functions of life and biological mechanisms. Vaucanson was the most important of them with his famous robots, which have since been lost: they included *The Flute Player, The Tambourine and Flageolet Player* and *The Digesting Duck*.

*104*

The culmination of such creations was *The Dulcimer Player,* an android automaton made in 1784 for Marie Antoinette by the mechanist Kintzing and the cabinet-maker Roentgen. This dulcimer has 46 strings and the musician can play eight tunes. The mechanism, which was placed under the stool on which the figure sits, consists mainly of a mainspring and a brass cylinder with 16 longitudinal cams and 16 rows of rods. With the help of levers, cams control the figure's forearms while the rods dictate the movements of the hammers. Beyond the complexity of the mechanism and the reproduction of human movement, the appeal of this piece lies in its aesthetic quality and it is a genuine work of art.

The invention in 1796 by Antoine Favre of a mechanism operated by the vibration of strips of metal enabling music to be played, allowed mechanisms to be miniaturised while still using a large number of notes. This

*105*

revolution made possible the numerous musical-boxes produced from the nineteenth century until the present day. Equipped with one of these mass-produced movements whose motor also activated the rods animating the little figures, these boxes brought the delights of automata to the

*106*

general public. The automated toys made by Fernand Martin in the 1880s made fun of his contemporaries and portrayed the society of that time. A hairdresser, a strongman from the fun-fair and a lawyer scuttle around with jerky, caricatured movements. These figures also highlight the fundamental changes that occurred in this period, such as the democratisation of toys, new methods of commercial distribution and mass production using cheap industrial materials. In the twentieth century, the

*107*

splendid and enigmatic tightrope walker made by Decamps in 1934 perpetuated the great tradition of eighteenth-century automata.

## Mechanisation

Following the initial studies and successes of the eighteenth century, the first half of the nineteenth century was the golden age of the machine-tool. Now made of metal, these machines facilitated industrial mechanisation and the precision machining of large components. Machine-tools diversified with the development of mortise machines, and planing, drilling and milling machines, and were used in the making of every component in industrial machines. British manufacturers were the leaders in this field with Fox, Maudslay, Fairbairn and Whitworth. Whitworth's machines, which were acquired by the Conservatoire at the time of the Great Exhibition in London in 1851, show the advances made by British mechanical engineers and the modernity of their machines. They

*103.* Skeleton clock playing flutes and chimes, 1790. Inv. 10619

*105.* Chinese figure playing the barrel-organ, mid-19th century. Height: 23 cm. Inv. 20402

*106. The Gymnast,* toy automaton by Fernand Martin, *c.* 1890. Inv. 14177/86

*104. The Dulcimer Player,* a musical automaton made in 1784 by the mechanical engineer Kintzing and the cabinet-maker Roentgen for Marie-Antoinette. Inv. 7501

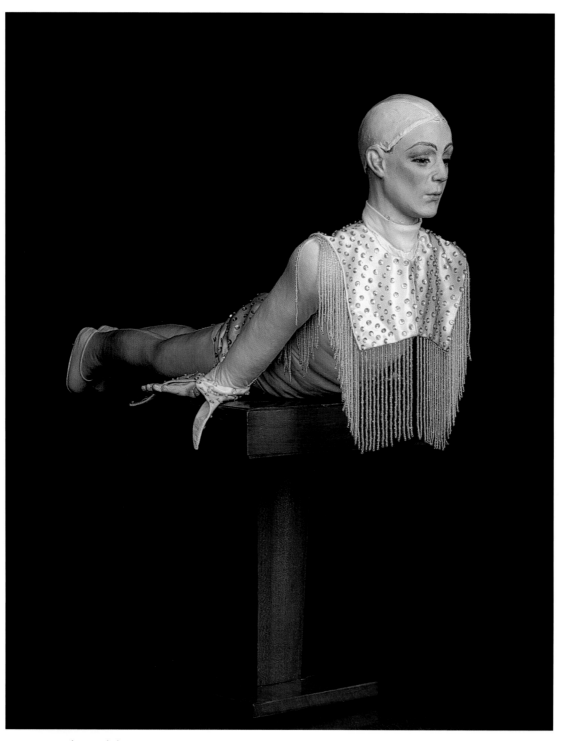

*107.* Acrobat made by Decamps, 1934.
Inv. 16845

*108.* Planing machine by J. Whitworth
and Co, Manchester, bought by the
Conservatoire at the Great Exhibition
in London in 1851. Inv. 5269

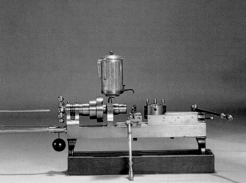

*109.* Exterior right conical gear, wooden model made for Théodore Olivier, professor of descriptive geometry at the Conservatoire, *c.* 1840. Inv. 4421

*110.* Model of a screw-cutting lathe with turret head, made by Brown and Sharpe from Providence (USA), 1878. Inv. 9110

*108* established the shapes and functions for machine-tools for almost a century. At the same time, technologists such as Hachette, Borgnis and Reuleaux were trying to synthesise elementary mechanisms so as to form a basic grammar enabling the conceptualisation of all machines. Descriptive geometry developed out of Monge's work and stood at the crossroads between mathematics and design. It was intended as a common language used by mechanists and engineers when they design or think up the parts for all sorts of machines. Théodore Olivier, the first *109* professor of descriptive geometry at the Conservatoire, worked on plans for gears and made a series of wooden models of gears showing all kinds of cogs and their teeth for the Museum.

## Mechanics in the Home

In the second half of the nineteenth century, industrial development enabled the mass production of new objects which brought profound *112* changes to daily life. Sewing machines, typewriters, calculating machines, cycles, coffee-grinders and food-mills were developed, patented and manufactured in huge quantities. The sewing machine is a significant example of this development. Invented by Barthélémy Thimonnier in 1830, it was intended to be used by the clothing industry as well as at home. It was still a complicated and unwieldy machine and was unable to equal the quality of handmade goods; it also generated opposition from workers who feared competition, as had also happened with Vaucanson's machines fifty years earlier. In addition to technical innovations that increased its reliability, three innovations assured the sewing machine's success. The simplification of its mechanism and the use of standardised and interchangeable parts made mass production possible and meant that the machine was easier to maintain. The resulting drop in price made certain that its use would spread to all sections of the population. At last, perfected and 'domesticated', it became an everyday object which fitted into domestic surroundings and encouraged the idea of the perfect housewife. In order to adapt to the needs of mass production, machine-tools developed in their turn. Mass production required machine-tools which could carry out several successive operations on the same component, thus ensuring greater precision and speed in the production process by means of reducing the handling and repositioning of the parts. These new machines were of course developed in the USA, which took the lead in mass production at the end of the nineteenth century. The screw-cutting lathe *110* developed by the Americans Brown and Sharpe was equipped with a turret lathe carrying six different tools and a transverse carriage for two different tool-carriers. It was consequently able to carry out several consecutive operations. The addition of a control system a few years later allowed for automated production and opened the way for programmable machines, while the electric motor provided flexibility and independence and allowed the reorganisation of workshops.

In parallel to this move towards mass production, research in mechanical engineering was also continuing. The collection of 'rolling curves' de-*111* signed by Schroeder constitute a kind of mechanist's masterpiece. These strangely-shaped gears show the contemporary state of knowledge on the subject in the placing of the curved teeth of the cogs and also in the way they were made. The components that transmit force to the machines constituted another area of research. Bearings were improved to reduce friction as much as possible. Advances in metallurgy meant that at the beginning of the century ball-bearings, rollers and needles came to replace old, smooth bearings and had a considerably longer life-span while also making lubrication easier.

Today, through the combined influence of computing and electronics, mechanics is undergoing a profound transformation. The skills it involves have developed and diversified. It is present everywhere, and is constantly changing face. Mechanics has been used to enable the miniaturisation of mechanisms, and has developed complex systems that give

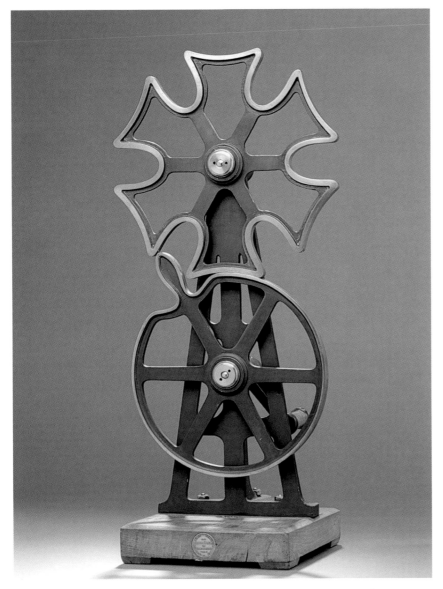

*112.* Barthélémy Thimonnier's sewing machine, 1830. Inv. 7955

*111.* Maltese cross mechanism by Schroeder, shown at the Universal Exhibition in Paris in 1867. Inv. 7781

machines great flexibility and make them easier to use. Productivity is now more a matter of control than of power, and automation has taken over from man in the control of machines.

In line with the historical perspective it favours, the Museum presents the contemporary equivalents of machine-tools by demonstrating the significance of computer-operated industrial robots capable of undertaking different tasks; of machine-parts such as ball-bearings which are still essential today, are ever more precise and have benefited from advances in materials; and, finally, of industrial micromechanical engineering.

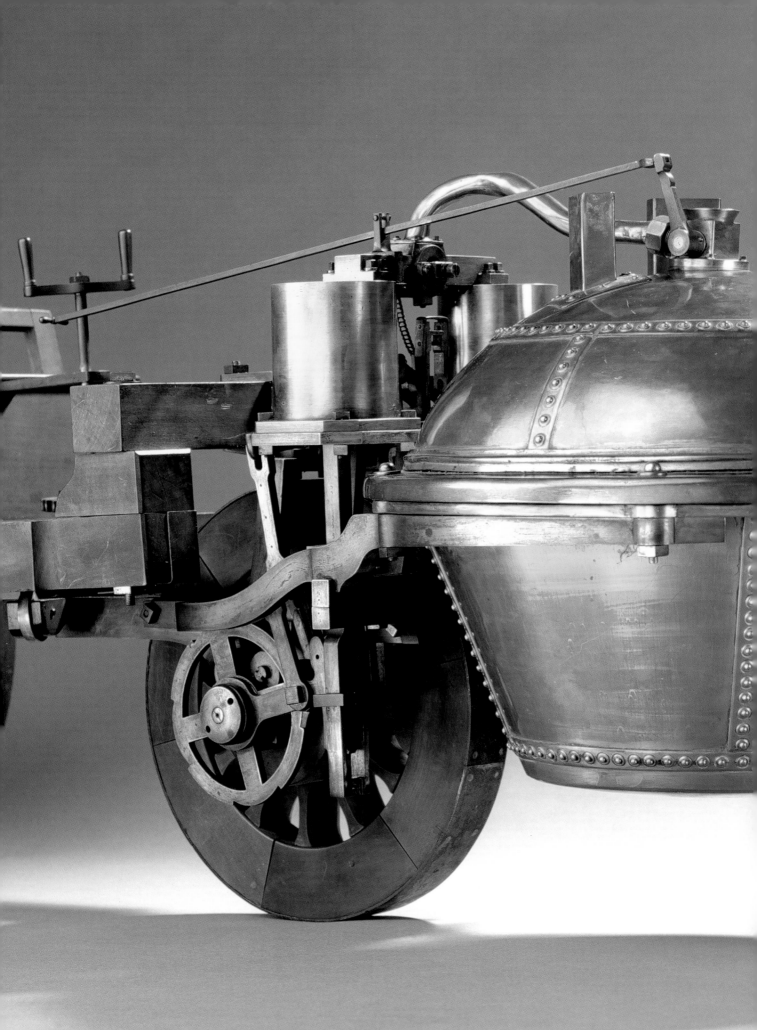

# Transport

In the history of mankind, transport is the domain in which the strictest industrial or commercial logic has most often been found side by side with the most irrational desires, in particular a desire to visit far-off places with no real reason. The conquest of space, which has gripped the industrialised world, is the most obvious example of this. What necessity justified man setting foot on the moon? Nowadays of course we are reaping the benefits of this adventure when we receive hundreds of television channels by satellite or communicate instantly across the planet. But most of all this quest stemmed from man's deep-rooted need to con-

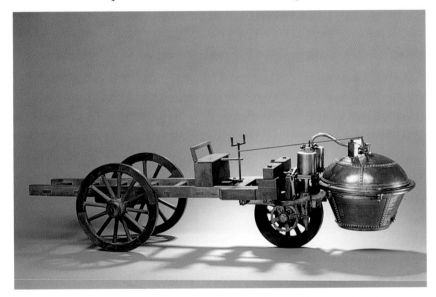

*113.* Cugnot's *fardier*, a steam-powered dray, model on a scale of 1 to 6, early 19th century. Inv. 4552.
*Opposite:* detail of the steam engine and its transmission

stantly expand his horizons. Today, physical travel has partly given way to 'virtual' travel, but for a very long time the conquest of the earth by various means of transport was a challenge that gave rise to spectacular inventions. As well as the technical progress achieved, the new means of transport, especially railways, led us to rethink our concept of space by creating interlinked networks. From military victories to paid holidays, the changing geography of our modern life-style owes a great deal to progress in the transport domain.

## From Dirt Track to Railway Track

The Musée des arts et métiers houses a large number of machines that owe as much to fantasy as they do to humdrum reality. Cugnot's *fardier* 113 is a very vivid illustration of this. Admittedly, when Nicolas-Joseph Cugnot (1725–1804) embarked upon his extraordinary attempt to create a 'steam-driven carriage' in 1769, the justification he gave was social and even patriotic, suggesting to the war minister a steam engine that could replace horses, thus avoiding the usual problems of working with animals. Did he realise just how many obstacles he would have to overcome in order to install on a vehicle one of these monstrous steam engines, which had never before left their solid foundations? With perseverance, the engineer solved all the technical problems one by one and made a full-scale prototype, which was saved from destruction just in time to be placed in the chapel of the Conservatoire at the turn of the nineteenth century. Did the prototype ever work? It is impossible to know. It certainly could have worked had this military engineer been given more

114. Model of a field kitchen with accessories. Length: 1.42 m. Inv. 14571

115. Seguin's locomotive with its double crank-axle and its tender, model on a scale of 1 to 6, 1829. Height: 50 cm. Inv. 12151. *Opposite:* detail

money. But not all the pitfalls were sorted out, especially the problem of steam consumption which meant that the engine had a very limited range and so was unsuitable for the needs of an army in the field.

*114*

Cugnot's machine had no successors: even the existence of his research remained secret because it was to do with defence. Yet his idea did have a future. The road was quite simply not the best surface for a mobile steam engine. British engineers worked this out about twenty years after Cugnot's experiments by developing the first steam locomotives to run

on rails – the only way to support the enormous weight of the machines. Despite the undeniable technical progress made by the British pioneers, some French engineers made impressive advances, such as the tubular boiler invented by Marc Seguin (1786–1875), the first in a celebrated family of engineers in the nineteenth century. Seguin's 1827 locomotive was the first machine with a tubular boiler, and its efficiency was considerably improved by this major innovation as well as by two large fans which amplified the draught in the firebox. Seguin's locomotive represented a *115* significant step towards increasing the power of the first locomotives. Within a few years these two innovations could be found in all locomotives and stationary steam engines.

With the first years of the railways, the geography of Europe, and later of the USA, was rapidly and completely transformed. An increasingly dense network linked all the major cities and the regions. The quest for speed had now begun, with the appearance of fast locomotives such as the *Crampton,* invented in 1843 by the British engineer Thomas Crampton, but which found success on the French railways, especially the Paris-Lyon-Méditerranée line, the famous PLM, which, in the mid-nineteenth century, was already dedicated to achieving high speed. By the end of the century the *Crampton* – with its two propulsive wheels measuring more *116* than two metres in diameter and positioned behind the furnace – could carry its passengers at more than a hundred kilometres an hour along the great straight railway lines of the Rhône valley.

The expansion of the French railway network reached its peak during this period and the new challenge for the railways was to find new sources of energy to drive the trains. Electricity made its appearance on curious hybrid locomotives such as Heilmann's *Rocket* of 1894, which had a *117* generator and electric motors fed by a steam engine. This new means of transmission helped to make all the axles propulsive and thus to increase the adherence and power of the machine. These first experiments led much later to the establishment of the electric grid that we use today with its overhead lines.

*118.* Model of a signalbox of the Saxby type, late 19th century. Height: 25 cm.
Inv. 16761–4

### Steam and Navigation

We should not allow the remarkable expansion of the railways to eclipse the waterways, and the importance of steam both on canals and at sea. Indeed the steam engine's first public journey was on water, with Fulton's trials on the Rhône as early as 1803. Some thirty years later the *59, 60* Luxor obelisk, given to France by the Viceroy of Egypt, crossed the Mediterranean on a barge towed by a curious ship called the *Sphinx,* which was equipped with two means of propulsion: its sails framed a large funnel and two paddle wheels. At the heart of the schooner was a splendid engine which was made in Britain; a model of it on a scale of *120* 1 to 5, built in 1830 by Eugène Philippe, is preserved in the Museum, and shows both its technical and aesthetic qualities. In this period when mechanical engineering excelled, there were no objections to adorning the frame of the engine with Greek columns and turning the iron monster into a life-size machine theatre.

Less obtrusive, the rudder control system on the *Yaroslav,* a ship belong- *119* ing to the Russian navy, was fitted with the servo-motor developed by Joseph Farcot in 1863. This invention has had such widespread consequences that it is easy to forget the existence of the original. Indeed, one might argue that Farcot's servo-motor, which helped the enormous rud-

*116.* The *Atalante,* a Crampton locomotive, model on a scale of 1 to 10, 1884.
Length: 88 cm. Inv. 16717

*117.* Heilmann's *Rocket* locomotive, model on a scale of 1 to 10. Length: 1.78 m.
Inv. 13607

119. Steam rudder from the *Yaroslav*, an application of Farcot's servo-motor, model on a scale of 1 to 4, 1883. Inv. 9910

120. Steam engine from the *Sphinx*, model on a scale of 1 to 5 by Eugène Philippe. Inv. 2822

121. Hydraulic lift for barges at the Fontinettes lock, model on a scale of 1 to 20. Inv. 12029

ders on transatlantic liners to work efficiently with the assistance of steam, is the direct ancestor of power-steering in modern cars. Very often, systems such as this, used in an industrial context, end up sooner or later in our everyday lives.

When Jules Verne was writing, 'gigantism' had reached its peak and the size of machines was a spur to progress rather than a hindrance to it. The *121* lift for barges at the Fontinettes lock, which can still be seen near Arques in the Pas-de-Calais, was a popular curiosity in its time. The attempt to lift barges more than 13 metres by means of water-power, thus enabling

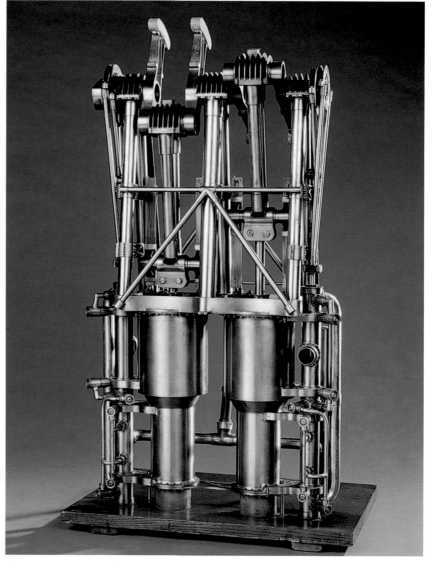

*122.* Clément Ader's steam engine for the *Eole 2*, 1893. Inv. 13561

them to navigate the uneven levels of the old Neuffossé canal, was a great success. The lift remained in operation until 1967 when a change in the size of barges forced it into retirement.

### The Conquest of the Air

How could one ever have imagined that the quest for power and glory would lead, in the 1890s, to the first flying machines? Visitors to the Museum often find it hard to believe that the engine built by the skilful engi-*122* neer Clément Ader to power his aircraft *Eole* was a steam engine fed by a spirit-fuel boiler. Because of the materials used in its construction, along with its design and amazing lightness, this engine has no reason to envy

*123.* Photograph of Clément Ader's 'Avion' Number 3, tested at the Satory military camp in 1897. Inv. 13560

*124.* Clément Ader's 'Avion' above the great staircase at the Musée des arts et métiers. Inv. 13560

modern car engines. But many advances had been made since Watt's engine, built a hundred years before, particularly as a result of the railways: the double-expansion steam engine, for instance, which meant that the propulsive power of steam could be used to maximum effect. It may seem strange that Ader resorted to a system that many would have found archaic at a time when De Dion's internal-combustion engine was already being used to power airships. However, in order to understand the deep-seated reasons for their decisions, we often need to imagine what it was like at the time and put ourselves in the shoes of these scientists. Ader's

*125.* The Deperdussin monoplane with a Gnome and Rhône 14-cylinder engine, model on a scale of 1 to 10, 1909. Inv. 14431

*126.* The 'Climber' motorcycle. Inv. 32033

first flight in 1890 was the result of many years of complex but cautious research, a slow maturation which did not allow for integrating radical changes in basic techniques. In addition, discretion was of the essence in this period of development, playing things close to one's chest by resorting to proven techniques, in this case the steam engine, rather than very new but still unreliable techniques such as the internal-combustion engine. Moreover, if paternity must be found for the nascent field of aeronautics, we should look towards the cycle rather than the locomotive. Because of their light structure and metal spokes, the bicycles of the 1870s made possible the first research on human flight. In 1867 Ader himself invented his *Véloce-caoutchouc,* a velocipede with a frame made of hollow iron tubes welded together which anticipated the light structures of his planes, which were also constructed from hollow tubes, this time made of light wood and silk.

The addition of an engine to the new cycles was a natural step and, very soon, engineers such as Félix Millet thought up original ways of doing this. As early as 1887, by putting a rotary engine, known by the poetic name of the 'Sun Wheel', in the back wheel of his motorcycle, Millet found a simple but ingenious way to ensure that the engine – with a cylinder of almost two litres in cubic capacity – took up as little room as possible. He even invented a hollow mudguard to use as a fuel tank as well as several other innovations which subsequently resulted in the success of the motorcycle. Like many of the engines exhibited in this 'museum of prototypes', Millet's motorcycle, soon forgotten, is a mere curiosity: little did the inventor know that, some twenty years later, it was his original rotary engine that would make the planes used in the First World War so efficient.

Like the car and the plane, the motorcycle benefited from the improved performance of engines and from their reduction in size, which gave rise to light and easy-to-handle vehicles such as the *Climber.*

Since the nineteenth century, railway networks have redrawn the maps in industrial countries. The development of the motor-car brought another, particularly intricate, network: roads. At the end of the twentieth century, the traveller can choose from almost too many means of transport: the car and other forms of road transport for short and medium-distance journeys; the high-speed TGV, or its equivalent, and other trains, which in some instances are in competition with planes, for medium- and long-distance journeys. The key challenges in the modern-day transport of people and goods are the automation of driving – first of cars, and ultimately of all forms of road transport – and improving connections between the various transport networks. The model of Roissy-Charles-de-Gaulle 2 airport, which ends the section on transport, is a perfect example of a place where different modes of transport meet: you can leave your car and catch a plane a few minutes later, or get off a local train to get on a high-speed TGV and travel across Europe. In France, only river transport has lost the important role it had for many centuries. On most canals, barges carrying coal, sand or grain have made way for pleasure boats – an agreeable way to spend time in an increasingly leisure-oriented society. As travelling times decrease, we are discovering new ways of taking our time.

*127.* Félix Millet and his tricycle with revolving cylinder engine and resilient wheel, 1887

# Machines in a Chapel

'To enter the Conservatoire des arts et métiers in Paris, you first cross an eighteenth-century courtyard and step into an old abbey church, now part of a later complex, but originally part of a priory. You enter and are stunned by a conspiracy in which the sublime universe of heavenly ogives and the chtonian world of gas guzzlers are juxtaposed.' The universe described by Umberto Eco in his book *Foucault's Pendulum* still exists, and when we enter the church today the first thing we see is the thirteenth-century choir. A walk through the ambulatory reminds us of the key periods in the building's history and of its former lives: the Merovin-

*129.* The *Blériot XI,* the plane used for the first crossing of the Channel, 1909. Inv. 14272

gian basilica, the rebuilding of the abbey in the eleventh century, the decorative work carried out in the seventeenth century and, finally, the major transformation when Saint-Martin-des-Champs was given over to a new religion: progress. The chapel, the showpiece of the Musée des arts et métiers during the nineteenth century, became a 'theatre of working machines' and even, through the impetus of General Morin, an experimental laboratory which was described as a miniature factory by his astonished contemporaries. Today the turbines have breathed their last, but the presence and imagination of visitors to the Museum bring back to life the extraordinary prototypes that line the great nave.

*128.* Scale model of the Statue of Liberty. Works in plaster on the enlargement of the original model. Inv. 13768/2

## A Century of Engines in a Church

Suspended high above are the planes developed by adventurers such as Esnault-Pelterie, Breguet and Louis Blériot. The *Blériot XI,* the plane *129* which crossed the Channel, has been here since 1909, when it made its ceremonial entrance into the Conservatoire des arts et métiers, this 'Pantheon of technical inventions'. It is a monoplane 8 metres long and with a wingspan of 7.8 metres and has a fuselage made of ash and poplar reinforced with piano-wire. Its 25-horsepower W-engine, which was developed by Anzani in 1909, enabled Blériot to accomplish his historic feat that same year. The wooden propeller is 2.08 metres in diameter and, at the back, the plane has a steering rudder controlled by the pilot's foot and an altitude rudder. Its restoration, particularly that of the oil-cloth on the wings, required the patient labour of a team with a variety of skills. The total weight of the plane, including the pilot and enough petrol to fly for two hours, is about 300 kilograms. On 25 July 1909, Louis Blériot took off from Sangatte near Calais at 4.35 a.m., crossed the Channel and reached Dover in 38 minutes.

After plane engines came rocket engines. Thanks to the gift from the So-

*130.* The *Obéissante,* the first steam bus, 1873, built by Amédée Bollée. Inv. 16851

ciété Européenne de Propulsion, the Museum is able to display a full-scale model of the Vulcan engine used to power the main stage of the *Ariane 5* rocket. The model shows an early version of the engine from 1980, when it was only supposed to operate in a vacuum. Today the engine is ignited on lift-off, and the nozzle has been shortened to enable it to run in the atmosphere. The thrust, which was previously 60 tons, has been increased to 110 tons. As a museum designed to house prototypes and technical innovations, it is the duty of the Musée des arts et métiers to display these steps in the process of innovation, which are common to every scientific and technical advance.

### From the 'Obéissante' to the Statue of Liberty

But let us return to earth so that we can admire the marvellous machines that are milestones in the story of the motor-car: Amédée Bollée's *Obéissante,* Leyat's car with a propeller and, a more recent example, the magnificent Hispano-Suiza. In 1873, the Obéissante travelled at 30 kilometres per hour with 12 passengers; there was a driver at the back and a pilot at the front, and the two were linked by an acoustic system so that the pilot could warn the driver to increase the pressure before they climbed any hills. This steam omnibus completed the 230 kilometres

*131.* The chapel in the Thirties. The Statue of
Liberty towers above the large vehicles

between Paris and Le Mans in 18 hours, including stops to pick up water and food. The boiler was fed with water by means of a pump that drew water from the tender while the machine was running, or from streams during the stops that had to be made every ten kilometres in order to fill up the tank.

Back in the chapel, the Obéissante has ended its journey at the feet of the Statue of Liberty; a strange maiden to find in a place like this, she was given to the Conservatoire in 1908 by Bartholdi's widow. This model (on a scale of 1 to 16) of *Liberty lighting up the world,* the statue which illuminated New York's harbour on 28 October 1886, was the fruit of the dreams and hard work of Auguste Bartholdi and Gustave Eiffel. Bartholdi's bequest to the Museum also includes two magnificent models – 'Works in plaster on the enlargement of the original model of the head' and 'Assembling the head in hammered copper' – which keep alive the memory of the huge amount of work involved in making the statue. The successive enlargements of the initial model made by Bartholdi in 1875 were carried out in the workshops of Gaget, Gautier & Co, and marked the Parisian landscape for ten years. The statue is one of the highpoints of metal construction, and its structure – a copper membrane suspended on an iron skeleton – was so innovative that it was adopted by architects during the 20th century. But the statue also belongs to the imaginary world of the Museum: the hero in Umberto Eco's novel thinks about hiding in the sentry box inside the pedestal before opting for a safer place in the periscope upstairs.

### The Pendulum

Leon Foucault (1819–1868) is the perfect example of the intuitive and diligent experimenter whose work the Conservatoire is proud to possess. His gyroscope and device for measuring the speed of light joined the collection in 1869, together with the three pendulums he made with the help of the instrument-maker Gustave Froment. The principle of the pendulum – a suspended weight moving in a vertical plane with isochronal oscillations – is simple. What remained was to provide experimental proof of the Earth's rotation, which could be done by putting a pendulum in a place specially adapted for this demonstration. 'Have you seen the earth turn? Would you like to see it turn? Go and see it on Thursday, and every following Thursday until further notice, from 10 a.m. until noon, at the Panthéon. The brilliant experiment thought up by Léon Foucault takes place here, in the presence of the public, in the best conditions in the world; and the pendulum, suspended by the expert hand of M. Froment from Soufflot's cupola, demonstrates to all eyes the rotary movement of our planet.' On 26 March 1851 the front page of the *National* was given over to this extraordinary event. The sphere used in the experiment is now in the Museum and a recent X-ray showed that it was composed of nothing but two hollow brass half-shells, with a matching central ring and held together by a threaded rod. The pendulum swinging in the chapel dates from 1855 and is the one that was put on display at the Universal Exhibition, where it was kept in motion automatically by an electromagnetic device. The sphere, suspended by a thread 18 metres long, weighs 25 kilograms. Finally, the Museum has a third pendulum, the very first one tried out by Foucault in his basement at 28 rue d'Assas. This steel sphere weighing 19 kilograms is also part of the bequest made to the Conservatoire in 1869 by his mother.

132. Foucault's pendulum (1855) in the chapel of the Musée des arts et métiers

## Drawings of Machines

From its creation, the Conservatoire des arts et métiers, an exhibition gallery for machines and models, also housed a drawing school which was useful in recording the entrance of different pieces into the collections. The collection of old drawings reveals objects which used to be exhibited in the Museum: *Bramah's Fire Engine, Kirchner's Dendrometer* and *Kettle's Weighing Machine.* The original drawings are more explicit than modern photographs and more adequately fulfil the educational function that is the primary task of the Museum. The chromatic conventions

4, 135

133, 134

of the late eighteenth and early nineteenth centuries – steel is represented by blue and blue-grey, brass by yellow, copper by reddish-brown, wood by brown, chestnut or tobacco-brown – contribute to the homogeneity of this remarkable iconographic collection.

Other drawings have now been added to the collection, those made with the help of a computer to represent certain pieces in the collection. The drawings of Scott's machine, an impressive steam engine made in 1860, are an example of this. Thanks to the Museum's partnership with the Technological University of Compiègne, these drawings can be exhibited alongside the reconstructed flywheel. This double-action, double-

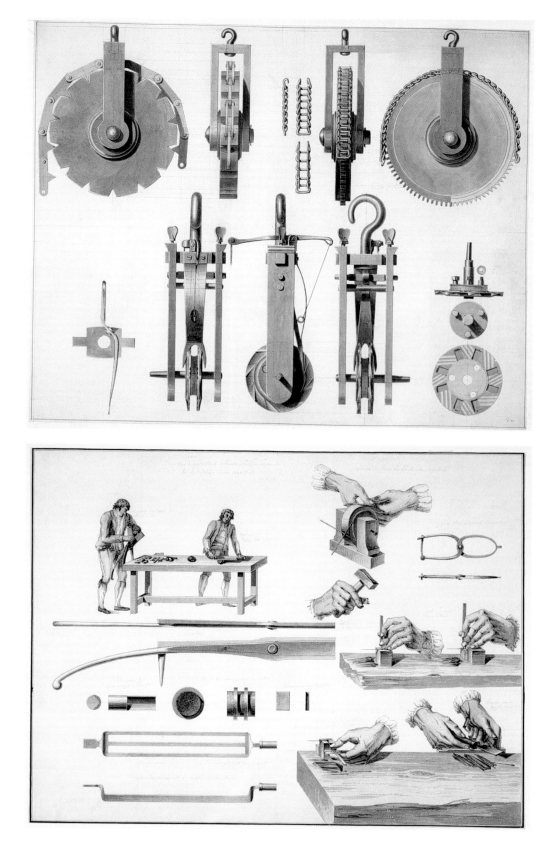

*133. Pulleys,* washdrawing, by Dromard, late 18th century. Inv. 13571.143/1

*134. Making Sewing Needles,* washdrawing, late 18th century. Inv. 13571.295/1

expansion steam engine was one of the last beam engines to be used in France.

## Between Emotion and Pedagogy

'A harsh tutor, Madame de Genlis', Louis Philippe confessed to Victor Hugo in one of the conversations related by the writer in 1847. At the request of this exceptional woman, the Périer brothers asked François-Etienne Calla to make the models now preserved in the Museum. Marvels of precision and ingenuity, they are an accurate reflection of the state of technical science in the eighteenth century, information that can also be found by looking at the plates in the *Encyclopédie*. But their

*136. Man with a Life-Belt*, watercolour, early 19th century. Inv. 13571.458

*135. Kirchner's Dendrometer,* watercolour with wash, 1804. Inv. 13571.466/3

significance is also more general. Because they give pride of place to the techniques employed in the workshops of the time, bearing witness to an unparalleled care and attention in the making of educational models, these objects have an irreplaceable topicality and charm. This is true of many objects and models in the Museum, often historical pieces, but at the same time educational tools, such as the wire models used to help teach descriptive geometry, which were requested by Théodore Olivier (1793–1853), professor then administrator of the Conservatoire des arts et métiers.

'All the arts have points of contact', declared the abbot Henri Grégoire, the founder of this Museum. A museum of technological innovation, set up in an abbey which became a centre for technical teaching and research, the Musée des arts et métiers remains to this day a unique institution whose main goal is to promote, through the exercise of memory, the exercise of the imagination and the spirit of invention.

# Index

## Bibliography

*La Revue,* quaterly review of the Musée des arts et métiers dedicated to the history and museology of technical innovations, 72 pages. Published since September 1992.

*Les Carnets,* collection of educational documents for teachers.

*Arts et métiers, l'album du Musée,* CD-ROM Mac/Windows compatible, Musée des arts et métiers, Productions La Forêt, 1995.

Butor, Michel and Dolémieux, Pascal, *Icare à Paris ou les entrailles de l'ingénieur,* Hachette, 1992.

Carrière, Jean-Claude and Séméniako, Michel, *Le sens de la visite,* Editions Carré/Musée des arts et métiers, 1997.

Ferriot, Dominique and Jacomy, Bruno, 'Le Musée des arts et métiers, problématique d'une rénovation', in *La Révolution de la Muséologie des Sciences,* edited by Bernard Schiele and Emlyn H. Koster, Presses Universitaires de Lyon, 1998.

Jacomy, Bruno, *Une histoire des techniques,* Editions du Seuil, Collection Points, 1990.

Mercier, Alain, *Un Conservatoire pour les arts et métiers,* Gallimard, Collection Découvertes, 1994.

Le Moël, Michel, Saint-Paul, Raymond and Fontanon, Claudine, *1794–1994, Le Conservatoire national des arts et métiers au cœur de Paris,* Conservatoire national des arts et métiers, délégation à l'Action artistique de la Ville de Paris, 1994.

## Contents

*Musées et Monuments de France*
Published with the support of the Fondation BNP PARIBAS

## Books in print

*Translation*
France Bennett

*Editing*
Jean McNicol
Rebecca Reid

*Photo Credits*
Hugo Maertens, Bruges
Fred Béhar (p. 1)
Pascal Dolémieux/Métis (fig. 3, 7, 8, 10, 11, 13, 124)
Dephti-Ouest (fig. 4, 64, 65, 133–136)
Jean-Claude Wetzel, studio CNAM (fig. 30, 74, 129, 130, 132)
Pascal Faligot (fig. 12, 36, 53, 66, 82, 110)

*Design*
Stéphan Alberty, Brussels

*Production*
Ludion, Ghent

© Musées et Monuments de France – 1998
Jean-Jacques Goron
41, Avenue de l'Opéra
75002 Paris
Tel. : 01 42 98 16 04
Fax : 01 42 98 14 11
© the artists, their heirs or copyright-holders.
Any copyright-holders we have been unable to reach or to whom inaccurate acknowledgement has been made are invited to contact the publisher.

ISBN 2–911809–16–5
Dépôt légal : September 1998
Reprint: 2002